"Was it necessary to kiss me like that?"

Anna spoke angrily when she was at last allowed to draw her breath.

"Kissing a woman is always the best way to silence her effectively," Scott replied without hesitation, his voice mocking.

"I don't think I ever want to see you again," she exclaimed, struggling against him for release. But his arms merely tightened around her.

"You will see me again, and very soon," he assured her bluntly. "You want me as much as I want you!"

Anna felt the shock of his words go through her as she realized it was true. She'd thought her broken heart would never mend, but Scott's kisses made her forget that another man had ever existed.

The Man from Amazibu Bay

by

YVONNE WHITTAL

Harlequin Books

TORONTO • LONDON • LOS ANGELES • AMSTERDAM
SYDNEY • HAMBURG • PARIS • STOCKHOLM • ATHENS • TOKYO

Original hardcover edition published in 1980
by Mills & Boon Limited

ISBN 0-373-02358-8

Harlequin edition published September 1980

Printed in U.S.A.

CHAPTER ONE

THE lecturer's voice droned on monotonously in the large ante-room leading off the main lounge in the Caribbean Hotel, but Anna Lindsay was no longer listening. This was the third and final day of the seminar on hotel accountancy which Morris Porter had insisted she should attend, but the lecture was no longer interesting or informative, and her thoughts began to wander, as if along a well-trodden path, to her arrival in Durban, and the many weeks of painful soul-searching which had followed.

On the advice of her parents she had left Johannesburg to take up this position as receptionist-bookkeeper with Morris Porter who, with the help of his wife Sheila, managed the Caribbean on the Durban beach-front. Morris and Sheila had been friends of her parents for many years and, desperate as they were at the time to find someone suitable to fill the position, they had welcomed Anna with an eagerness which had been deeply touching.

Anna, who had been content for some years to remain in the employ of a firm of accountants, grasped at the opportunity to cut herself adrift from the monotony of her job, but that had not been the only reason why she now found herself working for Morris and Sheila in South Africa's well-known coastal city. At the age of twenty-five it had been a drastic change for Anna to leave her family home and all the things she had cared about, but drastic measures had been called for at the time, and she did not regret these past six months at the

Caribbean. Work had kept her sane while she took an in-depth look at herself, and the woman she had become.

She looked up with a guilty start when the lecturer's voice halted abruptly, but he had turned towards the blackboard to demonstrate the point he was trying to make and, discarding her thoughts, she made a renewed effort to concentrate on what was being said. The lecture continued, but this time it was not her turbulent thoughts which prevented her from listening attentively; it was the curious sensation that she was being observed. Keeping her eyes riveted upon the lecturer, she tried to ignore this growing awareness. She was accustomed to being stared at by the opposite sex and, since she was the only woman among twenty-odd men in that room, it was not unnatural that they would glance at her from time to time, but this was something quite different.

A prickling sensation rose from her spine up to her scalp and, unable to prevent herself, she turned her head slightly and found herself staring directly into a pair of disconcerting blue eyes that did not waver for one second. Anna sustained the man's glance in a coldly detached manner, but there was no sign of embarrassment on his lean, deeply tanned face at being caught staring, and it was *she* who was finally forced to look away.

This was not the first time she had come practically face to face with Scott Beresford in the Caribbean over the past six months. Considering that he owned the Caribbean, as well as several other hotels along the Natal coast, his presence there was not unusual, but why he should have looked in on the seminar she had no idea, and when she glanced round again a few minutes later he had gone.

It was at a congress of hoteliers which was held in the Caribbean that she had first noticed Scott Beresford, but this had hardly been surprising, for he had been taller than most of the men attending the congress, and exceptionally good-looking with sleek dark hair which had been severely disciplined because of a strong tendency to curl. He was perfectly proportioned, with broad shoulders tapering down to slim hips, and she had judged him to be about thirty-four, but at that point her casual observation had ended. No man would ever succeed in capturing her interest again in the way Andrew Tait had done. Her life had revolved around Andrew for many years; years during which she had loved him in unfaltering silence only to discover eventually that he preferred someone else. The pain of it was something which, after six months away from Johannesburg, she was only just beginning to accept as something she would have to live with for the rest of her life.

During the lunch break Anna went to her usual table in the dining-room and ordered something light. Inactivity never enhanced her appetite, only her thought processes, and that was something she wanted to avoid at all costs.

"May I join you?"

She looked up with a start to see Scott Beresford, immaculate in a lightweight summer suit, pull out a chair and seat himself opposite her and, ignoring the fact that he had it within his power to fire her, she glanced about the room and said coldly, "There *are* other tables."

"The company of a beautiful woman always helps my food to digest," he replied with a smile that infuriated her instantly.

"An antacid could do the same for you."

"I don't believe in wasting money when I can obtain a cheaper remedy," he insisted blandly, and she almost choked with anger as he placed his order with the waiter and turned to her once again, allowing his appreciative glance to slide over her. "I'm Scott Beresford," he introduced himself, "and you're Anna Lindsay, not so?"

She met his blue gaze with a steadiness that surprised her. "You've obviously been doing some investigating."

"I always investigate people who interest me," he informed her mockingly.

"There's nothing about me which could possibly interest someone like yourself." she said tritely, loath to admit that she found his deep voice pleasing on the ear.

His sensuous mouth curved into a brief smile. "That's where you're wrong. You're a very attractive woman, and you must be well aware of the way men look at you."

"I am aware of it, yes, but I must admit that they're a little more subtle about it, and have never stared at me quite so brazenly," she replied coldly.

His disconcerting eyes mocked her. "Have I appeared brazen, then?"

"You know very well you have," she accused sharply, her antagonism towards this man increasing with every passing second.

"Why should I hide the fact that I find you attractive?"

Anna was ready with a scathing reply, but their lunch was served and she remained silent instead. Scott Beresford made no attempt at further conversation either, but she was acutely conscious of the fact that she was being closely observed, and she could not make up her mind whether to feel flattered or irritated.

When their tea had been served he remarked casually, "You weren't concentrating on the lecture this morning."

"The lecture was elementary and mostly repetition."

"But interesting, nevertheless," he insisted, offering

her a cigarette from the gold case he had taken from his jacket pocket, but she shook her head and he lit one for himself.

"We were told nothing this morning that I didn't know already," she told him quite frankly.

"You speak as though you've had prior experience."

She shrugged carelessly. "I was employed by a firm of accountants in Johannesburg for a few years before I joined the staff of the Caribbean, and there was very little in this morning's lecture of which I had no knowledge."

She raised her glance at that moment and met Morris Porter's over the heads of the other diners and, smiling broadly, he made his way towards her amongst the tables.

"I had no idea you knew Anna, Mr. Beresford?" Morris remarked with some surprise when he reached their table.

"I met Miss Lindsay this morning when I sat in on the lecture for a few minutes," Scott told him smoothly.

"If I'd known you would be staying to lunch, Mr. Beresford –"

"I hadn't intended staying either, Morris," Scott interrupted, his humorous glance meeting Anna's. "When Miss Lindsay invited me so charmingly to join her, I found myself accepting."

Anna was rendered speechless for the first time in her life, but her green eyes flashed angrily at him for twisting the truth so deliberately and outrageously.

Morris glanced a little curiously at her, but when she offered no explanation he asked, "How is the seminar progressing?"

"It's been a little boring this morning, thank you, Morris," she replied almost accusingly.

"I was afraid it might be," he admitted ruefully, turning towards Scott and gesturing dramatically. "You know, Mr. Beresford, you have Anna to thank for the Caribbean's books and accounts being in such perfect order."

Anna was not averse to praise, but at that moment it embarrassed her to have Scott Beresford's attention focussed on her so intently, and she said a little haughtily, "Flattery won't pay my accounts, Morris."

Morris grimaced and tapped her playfully on the cheek with his fingers. "Women are all the same – they show their claws at the most unexpected moment! Excuse me," he added, grinning as he beat a hasty retreat.

Anna watched Morris's tall, slightly stooped figure until he disappeared through the swing doors and, without her realising it, her lips curved into a smile which altered the usual austerity of her expression, but it lasted only a brief moment before she turned cold, heavily lashed green eyes on the man seated opposite her.

"You have no right to tell Morris I'd invited you to have lunch with me. It was a downright lie, and you know it."

"Does it matter?" Scott queried impatiently, gesturing with his hands as if to brush aside her protest. "Will you have dinner with me this evening?"

Startled by his invitation, she was silent for a moment before she said offhandedly, "Considering that I live here in the Caribbean as well as work here, I dare say we shall see each other at dinner if you're still about."

"You know very well that I was referring to having dinner elsewhere." He gestured impatiently once again with a strong, well-shaped hand that was as tanned as his complexion, but Anna preferred to remain distant.

"But I hardly know you, Mr. ... er ... Beresford."

"The name is Scott, and you know that already," he

said abruptly. "And I'm asking you to dine with me, Miss Lindsay, not to go to bed with me."

Anna gasped audibly. "Are you always so shockingly outspoken?"

"If it helps the other person to know where they stand, yes," he said curtly, his eyes narrowing as they met hers. "Do you have dinner with me this evening or don't you?"

A refusal sprang to her lips, but she hesitated as a devilish little voice whispered inside her, 'Why not? Scott Beresford is attractive and you have nothing better to do. He most probably won't bother with you again after tonight, so why not spend an entertaining evening in his company instead of brooding away the hours in your room?'

"I would like to have dinner with you, thank you," she heard herself reply, much to her own disgust, and, when his eyebrows rose sharply, she added, "You seem surprised."

"I didn't expect you to agree so readily."

"Have I disappointed you?" she mocked him, and saw a derisive little smile curve his lips.

"On the contrary, I like women who make up their minds quickly." They left the dining-room and as the swing doors closed behind them he said: "I'll be waiting for you here in the foyer at six-thirty."

Anna nodded coolly and they parted company, but during the lectures that afternoon she wondered if she had not been a fool to accept his invitation so hurriedly. He was the most disconcerting man she had ever met, and she was more than a little disturbed to discover that her pulse rate quickened each time she thought of him. He was a complete stranger, except for the knowledge that he owned the Caribbean and that she had seen him on a few occasions when he had called on Morris for business purposes, and she cursed her stupidity several times during the afternoon while she made an effort to concentrate on the lecture.

When she left the lecture-room later that afternoon she was beginning to regret that she had accepted Scott Beresford's invitation, but to change her mind would only evoke his mockery. His invitation had been a challenge, and she had accepted it, so, come what may, she would have dinner with him that evening, if only to prove to herself that she was capable of enjoying the company of other men besides ...! No! she decided, collecting her thoughts sharply. She did not want to think of Andrew and the many hours she had spent in his company before her young sister had returned home from college to bemuse him so completely. It was over and done with, she told herself, jabbing the elevator button fiercely and concentrating instead on what she would wear that evening.

There was a tentative knock on her bedroom door just after six that evening and Sheila Porter, her dark hair sprinkled liberally with grey, entered the room quietly and closed the door behind her.

"Dining out tonight, Anna?" she asked, her appreciative glance sliding over the richly embroidered silk evening gown which clung gently to the slender, supple figure seated in front of the dressing-table.

"Yes, I am," Anna confirmed, running a coral pink lipstick across her lips and pausing to study the effect. "I'm dining with Scott Beresford."

"You know who Scott Beresford is, of course, but I must warn you that he has a way with women, and I wouldn't want you to be hurt again."

Anna's glance met Sheila's in the mirror, and the concern in the older woman's eyes warmed her heart considerably. "Thanks for the warning, Sheila," she said gently. "I'm not unaware of Mr. Beresford's attractions, or his suave manner, but I'm not fooled by it either. I'm having dinner with him merely to get out for a while, and that's all."

"I'm glad."

"Glad, Sheila?" she questioned confusedly.

"I'm not too happy about your choice of companion, but I'm glad you're going out for a change instead of closeting yourself in your room," Sheila smiled. "It's about time."

"Hm ... I suppose so," Anna replied absently while she inspected her make-up in the mirror and pushed a stray curl into place.

Since her arrival in Durban she had had her reddish-gold hair trimmed to a more practical length which still enabled her to pin it back during the day as well as leaving it to hang loosely in soft waves about her face and shoulders on occasions such as this. Wearing her hair loose softened her features considerably, but the clear green eyes remained cool and slightly aloof, hiding the hurt which lay deep within her, like a wound which refused to heal.

"Morris and I were beginning to think you would never get over Andrew," Sheila remarked pleasantly, but a look of dismay flashed across her gentle face when Anna rose swiftly to her feet and pinned her down with a cold glance.

"I never *will* get over Andrew, and the fact that he's married to my sister makes no difference to how I feel!" she spat out the words.

"I'm sorry."

"No, *I'm* sorry," Anna insisted contritely, gripping the arms of the woman who had been like a second mother to her these past months. "If there's one thing I've learnt since coming here to the Caribbean, then it's humility. I had no right to take my frustration out on you."

"I understand, my dear, so don't let it trouble you," Sheila smiled warmly, her gentleness making Anna feel more than just a little ashamed of herself.

"How do I look?" she asked the older woman after an awkward little silence threatened.

"Beautiful," Sheila sighed, stepping back a little to inspect her, and envying Anna her flawless skin and surprisingly youthful curves. "But then you always do look beautiful, my dear, no matter what you wear."

A spark of humour flashed in Anna's eyes as she embraced the motherly woman spontaneously. "I wasn't exactly fishing for compliments, but thank you all the same."

"Well, I'd better get downstairs or Morris might think I've run out on him," Sheila remarked in her usual brisk fashion, but she paused for a moment before opening the door and smiled. "Enjoy yourself, my dear."

Anna frowned as the door closed softly behind her. Whether she would enjoy her evening with Scott Beresford, she still had to discover, but it was at least a beginning towards making a new life for herself. She could not sit about and mope for ever – it was not in her nature – but the pain and the longing would always be there to haunt her no matter what she did.

Scott Beresford was waiting in the foyer when she stepped from the elevator, and she had to admit, albeit reluctantly, that he looked striking in his perfectly tailored black evening suit and bowtie, with the frilly shirt front startlingly white in contrast. He smiled briefly, his blue gaze sliding over her appreciatively before he took her arm and led her out into the cool night air where he helped her into the Mercedes which was parked close to the entrance.

"I'd expected to be kept waiting this evening, but you were absolutely punctual," he remarked casually as he steered the car into the traffic. "I've never yet known a woman to be on time for an appointment."

"I have quite a thing about being punctual, but I suppose that comes from working so many years for a firm where everyone always insisted on punctuality and keeping to a strict routine."

"I can quite believe you're a great asset to the Caribbean."

Anna glanced at him swiftly, not certain whether he was mocking her or merely stating a fact, but his lean profile gave no indication of his thoughts, and she said rather stiffly, "I wouldn't call myself an asset exactly. I have a job to do, and I do it to the best of my ability."

Scott made no further comment and they drove through the streets in silence. He took the coastal road to a restaurant a little out of the city, and she was beginning to dread the evening with him if they were to spend it with these heavy, lingering silences between them. In the richly continental atmosphere of the restaurant he had selected, his mood altered and he kept the conversation going throughout the superbly served meal.

They discussed the lectures given at the seminar at great length, and he listened attentively when she imparted some of her own ideas on certain topics. He ordered liqueurs with their coffee and, after the two glasses of wine she had consumed during dinner, Anna felt decidedly lightheaded as she cupped her chin in her hand and faced him across the candlelit table.

"I seem to have talked quite a lot about my own ideas and theories this evening, so tell me about yourself for a change."

A smile flickered across his face. "What would you like to know?"

"Anything and everything you would care to tell me," she announced, trying to concentrate on the pearl buttons on his shirt front and not on his penetrating blue eyes.

"My home is at Amazibu Bay further south along the coast, and the house is practically on the beach."

"Amazibu Bay," she repeated slowly. "That's an odd name for a town."

"Amazibu is a Zulu word for waterlily," he explained tolerantly. "The waterlilies grow on the banks of the river and occasionally, when the river is in flood, they're washed out on to the beach. Hence the name Amazibu Bay."

"So it's really Waterlily Bay," she mused aloud, a faint smile curving her lips. "How quaint, and so very appropriate."

"I've always thought so, yes," he said quietly.

"You're not married, I suppose?"

"Widowed." His mocking glance slid over her smooth, creamy shoulders, and his eyes suddenly became pinpoints of fire licking her skin. "You're very beautiful, Anna."

"Thank you," she said coldly, straightening abruptly as she tried to ward off the onslaught of his magnetism. "Do you live alone in your house at Amazibu Bay?" she changed the subject hastily.

"My aunt lives with me and tolerates admirably the irregular hours I keep," he replied with a touch of mockery lurking about his sensuous mouth as he leaned towards her across the small table. "Did you know that when the light catches your hair in a certain way it sets it aflame?"

The warm caressing note in his voice sent a tremor along her nerves, but she remained distant. "We're discussing your home."

"You're much more interesting," he insisted, a gleam of mockery still lurking in his disturbing eyes. "How have you managed to remain single all this time? You must be ... twenty-one?"

"Twenty-five," she corrected abruptly with a proud tilt of her head.

His eyebrows rose slightly as if in surprise. "There must have been plenty of men who've wanted to marry you, or did you frighten them off with your distant attitude?"

"I wouldn't know," she said coldly, finding his probing questions distasteful.

"There must have been someone special," he continued, quite unperturbed by her manner, and Anna's temper flared,

"That's none of your business!"

"I should have realised you'd have a temper to match that red hair," he laughed softly just as the band started playing softly, enticing the diners on to the floor and, taking her hand, he drew her to her feet. "Let's dance."

Anna had never felt less like dancing, but there was no escaping the firm grip of his lean fingers crushing her own as he led her on to the dance floor and drew her into his arms. He held her suffocatingly close against the hardness of his body, and her nerve ends vibrated in protest at the unexpected contact with such overpowering masculinity.

"If you don't mind," she managed at last, sparks of anger in her wide green eyes, "I do like to breathe while I'm dancing!"

His arm about her waist slackened a fraction, allowing

her more freedom, but his soft laughter activated her pulses in the most aggravating way.

"You're very cool, Anna. Cool and aloof. But I think I like you that way."

"What exactly is that supposed to mean?" she demanded, suspicion tautening her nerves and making her steps falter.

"I've always enjoyed a challenge," he enlightened her with an arrogance that sent a flicker of fear through her, "and you're a challenge I'm finding difficult to resist."

There was a resolute quality about the square, jutting jaw that was at once painfully familiar. Andrew had looked like that the last time she had seen him, and then he had made it agonisingly clear to her that he intended to marry her sister.

"I realise that I haven't been quite fair to you, Anna," Andrew had said forcefully, "but whether you like it, or not, Debbie and I are going to be married."

In the face of such determination there had been nothing she could do or say to prevent her hopes and dreams from shattering into fragments about her. Debbie, several years younger than Anna, had blossomed into a vivacious young woman, and she had captured Andrew's heart in a way which she, Anna, had failed to do in five years, and this had been the most difficult part of it all to accept.

The dance ended and Scott kept his arm about her as he led her back to their table, but she was aware that he was glancing at her strangely.

"I have a feeling that you weren't with me just then," he accused lightly once they were seated, and Anna's lips curved into a mocking smile.

"Do you find it deflating to know that someone could be with you physically, yet not mentally?"

"Not in the least," he told her calmly, lighting a cigarette and observing her through a screen of smoke. "You're entitled to the privacy of your thoughts, just as I have thoughts which I don't wish to share with anyone."

His reply did not surprise her, for she supposed that, having been married, he would probably have moments, just as she had, when memories came flooding back to the surface of the mind to inflict pain, or bitter-sweet memories. She was suddenly quite inexplicably curious to know more about him, but she decided to respect his privacy just as she wished him to respect hers.

It was after midnight when they finally walked through the swing doors of the Caribbean, and the sleepy porter smiled broadly at Anna and Scott as they walked past him into the foyer. Scott thumbed the elevator button and they waited in silence for the elevator to descend to the ground floor, but it was not an uneasy silence, and Anna was too pleasantly tired to be nervous of being alone with him when the elevator eventually swept them up to the third floor.

'I shall be gone long before breakfast tomorrow morning, but I shall see you again some time, Anna," he said as they stood outside her door in the dimly lit corridor, and Anna, quite tall herself, found that she had to look up some considerable way to meet his glance.

"I don't think that's likely."

"Amazibu Bay isn't on the other side of the earth, you know," he laughed briefly, his teeth flashing white against the tan of his complexion. "It's a little more than an hour's drive from Durban."

"Don't waste your gasoline," she insisted, that quality of aloofness which hovered about her creating a tantalising aura of which she was quite unaware.

"To see you again would be worth the money spent."

She had agreed to have dinner with him that evening, but she was not prepared to encourage him further, and she made this quite clear in the bluntest fashion. "It was very nice of you to invite me to have dinner with you this evening, Scott, and thank you, but please don't bother to see me again unless it has to do with hotel business."

"It's no bother," he mocked her derisively, and then, quite unexpectedly, she found herself in his arms and being kissed with a breathtaking expertise that sent a shiver of emotion through her body before he released her. "Goodnight, Anna," he said softly, with an enigmatic smile playing about his lips, and a few moments later the elevator was taking him down to the foyer.

It was only as she closed her bedroom door behind her and switched on the light that she surfaced from her bemused state to touch her lips with exploratory fingers as if she expected them to be altered in some way. Andrew had kissed her often, but he had never kissed her in the way Scott had just done. Oh, how she wished that Andrew *had* kissed her like that – just once! she thought with a hungry yearning that was like an insatiable ache inside her. Perhaps, if she closed her eyes and relived those brief moments in Scott's arms, she could pretend that it was Andrew, but, to her annoyance, Andrew's features were replaced by Scott's, and it was the warm pressure of Scott Beresford's lips and arms she felt again.

"Oh, what's the use!" she admonished herself severely. "I'm behaving like a child, and tearing myself apart in the process."

Settling back into her usual routine the following day was almost a relief, and Anna gave no further thought to her encounter with Scott Beresford, but a bouquet of

white lilies arrived while she was having tea with Morris
and Sheila that morning, and it brought Scott sharply
into focus once again. Tearing open the small envelope
with fingers that trembled ridiculously, she extracted
the card.

"I shall see you again soon," she read, and it was
signed "Scott."

Anna lowered the card and stared at the lilies, not
knowing whether to be pleased or angry. It was the first
time anyone had sent her flowers, and although the experience was thrilling, it made her realise that Scott
Beresford was not going to be shaken off lightly.

"May we know the name of your admirer?" Morris
interrupted her thoughts, and she made a visible effort
to pull herself together.

"Scott Beresford sent them."

"I see ..." Morris murmured, his dark head, greying
in a distinguished fashion at the temples, tilted thoughtfully.

"I believe he's a widower," she remarked casually.

"He's been widowed for almost two years."

"What was his wife like?"

"I never met her," Morris said quietly. "Why?"

"I just wondered."

"It's so romantic to receive flowers," Sheila sighed
dreamily, casting an accusing glance in her husband's
direction. "Why don't you ever send me flowers,
Morris?"

"But, my darling, you receive flowers every day," he
protested in surprise.

"For the hotel, yes, but not for me – personally,"
Sheila argued determinedly, and Anna hid a smile as
Morris leaned towards his wife, gesturing helplessly.

"Sweetheart, we've been married twenty-six years –"

"Exactly!" Sheila interrupted firmly. "In twenty-six years you've sent me flowers only twice, and that was when our son and daughter were born."

"But you never told me you wanted flowers."

"You shouldn't have to be told," Sheila scolded him. "If you had just a scrap of romance in you, you'd have done so without there having to be a reason for it."

Floored by this remark, Morris groaned as he rose to his feet and headed towards the door. "I think I'm needed in the kitchen."

"Men!" Sheila laughed once he had gone. "They think romance is something you practise before the marriage only, but . . ." She stared down at her wedding ring which she twirled thoughtfully between her fingers. "Morris was never one for sending flowers even before we were married, now that I come to think of it."

"What do I do with these?" Anna changed the subject, indicating the bouquet of lilies.

"Put them in a vase, of course," Sheila stated definitely, but as the bell on the reception desk tinkled loudly, she picked up the bouquet and gestured expressively. "You go and attend to whoever that is, and I'll see to the flowers for you."

Relieved at being able to dispense with the flowers, and hoping that Sheila would hide them somewhere out of sight, Anna returned hastily to the reception desk. Her hopes were futile, however, for Sheila returned a few minutes later with the lilies arranged decoratively in a flat vase.

"There," she said, placing them on the counter where Anna could not fail to see the lilies every time she looked up. "Aren't they beautiful?"

"Beautiful," Anna echoed dully, unable to conjure up enough enthusiasm to match Sheila's.

She did not want to be reminded of Scott Beresford. Every time she thought of him, she recalled the way he had kissed her, and the memory of it had haunted her for some time before she had been able to fall asleep the previous night. He was a totally infuriating man!

CHAPTER TWO

ANNA had almost succeeded in forgetting Scott Beresford when an enormous bouquet of yellow chrysanthemums was delivered to her a week later, with a card on which there was typed: "Be ready at six-thirty. Have made arrangements for us to dine out. Scott."

It was an order, not an invitation, and, infuriated, she ripped the card to shreds and dropped the pieces into the wastepaper bin. The flowers would have followed it had Sheila not passed the reception desk at that moment, stopping to admire the perfect blooms.

"Scott Beresford again?"

"Yes," Anna said tritely. "He's made arrangements for us to dine somewhere tonight."

"Lucky girl," Sheila smiled, but Anna merely snorted angrily.

"The man's an infernal nuisance!"

"Most men are, my dear," Sheila replied humorously, raising her eyebrows in surprise as the flowers were dumped unceremoniously into her arms. "Shall I put them in a vase for you?"

"Yes, please, Sheila," Anna said agitatedly. "But put them somewhere I can't see them. In the ladies' lounge, for instance, or the kitchen. Better still, throw them in the garbage can."

"My dear! Such beautiful chrysanthemums!" Sheila muttered reprovingly. "I'll put them in the ladies' lounge as you suggested, but definitely not in the kitchen, or the garbage can."

A frown creased Anna's brow as she stared after Sheila's retreating figure, and she began to feel a little ashamed of herself. If Scott Beresford had taken the trouble to send her flowers, the least she could do would be to accept them gracefully instead of wanting to throw them away, she admonished herself severely. It was the invitation to dinner which had upset her. No, she corrected herself, it was the *instruction* that she was to have dinner with him which had angered her most of all. If he thought she would be only too eager to fall in with any and every suggestion he made, then he could think again! She was *not* going to be ready and waiting when he arrived at six-thirty that evening.

Sheila crossed the foyer a few minutes later with the bright yellow chrysanthemums beautifully arranged in a tall vase, and Anna acted upon a most irrational impulse.

"I think I've changed my mind," her voice halted Sheila in her stride. "I'll have them on the counter after all."

If Sheila thought her behaviour strange, she gave no indication as to her feelings as she placed the flowers on the counter and stood back to admire them.

"I was hoping you'd change your mind," she stated calmly, and Anna expelled the air from her lungs as she watched her disappear into Morris's office.

Feeling more than a little foolish, Anna drew the books towards her and tried to concentrate on her work. It was a woman's prerogative to change her mind, she tried to pacify herself, and she had done exactly that.

By five o'clock that afternoon, when the night staff took over, she still had not made up her mind whether she would go out with Scott or not. But somehow, once she reached the privacy of her room, she found herself mentally selecting a dress to wear for the occasion. Annoyed with herself, she went through to her bathroom and ran her bath water, but she was even more annoyed with herself when, half an hour later, she found herself changing into a pale green chiffon and wondering whether she should wear her pearls, or the diamond pendant her parents had given her on her twenty-first birthday.

"All right, admit it," she told herself when she sat down in front of the mirror to do her make-up. "You're going to have dinner with him this evening, but you're going to make quite sure that he knows this won't happen again."

Having confessed this to herself, she found it easier to accept her peculiar behaviour while she took her time with her make-up and did something with her hair. The time passed so quickly after that that she was surprised when the telephone beside her bed rang shrilly and she was told that Scott was in the foyer waiting for her. Picking up her wrap and her evening bag, she left her room, but her heart behaved in the oddest manner as the elevator took her down to the ground floor, It was nerves, she told herself sternly, and left it at that.

Scott was beside her the moment she stepped from the elevator, his eyes moving with deliberate slowness down the length of her, and giving her the sensation that he was actually touching her.

"You're even more beautiful than I remembered."

"You speak as though you haven't seen me for months ... and flattery will get you nowhere," she added coldly, but her senses reacted to the physical magnetism she was becoming increasingly aware of.

"This past week has felt like a year," he said, his hand warm and electrifying against her skin as he took her arm and led her towards the swing doors. A cynical little smile hovered about his mouth as he added caustically, "And you're still as sharp-tongued as ever."

"What did you expect?" she demanded indignantly. "You send me flowers, issuing an instruction that I should dine with you regardless of how I felt about it."

"You didn't have to accept," he reminded her mockingly as they stepped outside and walked to where he had parked the Mercedes.

"No, I didn't," she agreed bitterly, "but this is to be the last time, and I mean that!"

"We shall see," he smiled briefly, looking so infuriatingly self-assured as he helped her into the car that she tightened her fingers about her bag as the desire to slap his face raged through her.

The evening had started badly and seemed to continue in that vein. He had booked a table at the same restaurant they had gone to on the previous occasion, and during the meal the conversation remained brief and abrupt. She would make him understand, even if it killed her, that she had no interest in furthering their relationship. After what had happened between Andrew and herself she would never trust another man again, and least of all Scott Beresford. He was devilishly attractive, she had to admit, but she was not going to make a fool of herself again over any man.

Anna became aware of Scott observing her closely with intense interest, and she pushed her plate aside with a little more vigour than was really necessary.

"More wine?" he offered with a faint smile curving

his lips.

"No, thank you," she declined abruptly, making an effort to pull herself together.

"It might cool your temper, and help you to relax," he insisted, refilling her glass regardless of the fact that she did not want more.

"I am not in a temper, and I'm perfectly relaxed, thank you."

Scott refilled his own glass in silence and replaced the cork on the bottle before meeting her angry glance in an unperturbed manner. "You're trying to give me the brush-off, as they call it, but I knew from the moment I met you that I'd have to put up a fight for what I wanted."

Anna's nerves jarred uncomfortably, but she could not prevent herself from asking, "And what is it you want, may I ask?"

"You."

There was a soaring sensation in her ears as she stared at him with wide, incredulous eyes. "You have a nerve, I must say!"

"Then don't say it," he mocked, raising his glass. "Drink that wine. It will help you recover from the shock and settle your nerves."

"You're arrogant and insufferable!" she bit out the words, suppressing the desire to fling her glass of wine into his lean face.

"And you're the most beautiful creature I've ever seen when your temper is aroused," he replied calmly. "Drink up."

She *did* raise her glass to her lips then, swallowing down a mouthful of wine and almost choking on the fiery liquid as it passed along her throat, but it seemed to reach her blood-stream all too quickly and, to her further annoyance, the effect *was* relaxing.

"Shall we dance?" Scott asked eventually when the band resumed their playing after a few minutes break.

"No, thank you."

Scott's eyes gleamed with instant mockery. "But we danced together so beautifully last time."

"That was last time – this is *now*," she retorted stubbornly.

"What are you afraid of?"

Her head shot up defiantly, and her fiery green glance clashed with his. "I'm not afraid of anything, but I refuse to dance with you."

"Are you afraid your layer of ice might melt when I hold you in my arms?" he smiled cynically.

"You over-estimate yourself, Scott Beresford," she told him scathingly.

"Perhaps," he agreed smoothly, pushing back his chair and getting to his feet. "Dance with me and prove me wrong," he added, holding out his hand towards her.

She stared at it for a moment with indecision, then, accepting his challenge, she placed her hand in his and rose to her feet to walk with him on to the dance floor. At first his arm was light about her waist, but as the dance progressed, he drew her relentlessly closer, lowering his head to hers until his lips touched her ear. It was not accidental, she was certain, for his lips made little caressing movements against her ear-lobe.

"Don't hold me so close," she protested, fighting against the odd sensations quivering through her treacherous body.

"I like your perfume," he murmured, the deep timbre of his voice making her receptive nerves tingle. "It's like a breath of fresh mountain air, and most tantalising."

"Scott, *please*," she begged, straining a little against

him and despising the hint of breathlessness in her voice.

"You say that so beautifully," he persisted without obliging her. "Relax, Anna, I don't enjoy dancing with a wooden beam, and it's rather tiring on the arms." He raised his head then and the eyes that met hers were once again challenging. "You want to prove me wrong, don't you?"

Against her will, she relented and, to her dismay, found that she was actually enjoying herself. Scott danced well, as she had discovered on the previous occasion he had brought her to this restaurant and, despite herself, she found herself liking the feel of that strong arm about her, and the touch of his lips against her temple when she eventually succumbed to the temptation and lowered her head on to his shoulder.

How long they danced like that she did not know, but she was almost childishly disappointed when he finally released her and said: "Shall we go?"

She nodded mutely, and they went back to their table to collect her things in silence; a silence that lasted until Scott parked his car beneath the shadows close to the entrance of the Caribbean. Her fingers fumbled for the door-handle, but Scott anticipated her action and, leaning across her, he gripped her wrist firmly, sending faint tremors up the length of her arm and bringing her back sharply to reality.

"Don't go in yet," he said softly, his breath fanning her forehead, and Anna felt the latent antagonism rising within her.

"It's late, Scott."

"You're forgetting I shan't see you again for a few days."

"You're wasting your time," she said coldly, attempting to free herself from his clasp and failing. He was far

too close to her for her own peace of mind, and the
clean, warm scent of his body did something to her
senses.

"Being with you could never be considered a waste of
time," he insisted, his arm about her shoulders drawing
her against him despite her struggles.

"There must be other women —" she began, but his
lips found hers expertly in the darkness, stifling the rest
of her angry statement. Realising that her strength was
puny against his, she remained passive in his arms, forcing her lips to remain unresponsive beneath his, but
there seemed nothing she could do about the rapid increase of her pulse rate. When she was at last allowed
to draw a breath she demanded angrily, "Was it necessary to kiss me like that?"

"To kiss a woman is always the best way to silence
her effectively," he replied without hesitation, his voice
mocking her relentlessly.

"I don't think I ever want to see you again," she
exclaimed, struggling against him for release, but his
arms merely tightened about her.

"You're going to see me again, and very soon," he
assured her quite bluntly, and a wave of helplessness swept over her, making her cease her efforts to
escape.

"Can't you understand that I have no desire for your
company?"

Scott was silent for quite some time, and she was
almost beginning to think that she had succeeded in con-
vincing him when he released her abruptly, and said:
"Come on, I'll walk with you up to your room, just to
make sure no one snatches you along the way."

She clenched her teeth so tightly that her jaw ached,
but she allowed him to have his way for the last time.

His hand gripped her elbow firmly as he accompanied her inside, and he did not release her until they stood in the long, dimly lit corridor outside her door.

"Goodbye, Scott," she said firmly.

He stared for a moment at the slender hand she extended towards him, then his lips twisted derisively. "It's not goodbye, Anna, and I'll leave you this to remember me by."

Trapped as she was between the door and the hardness of his muscular body, the force of his kiss drove her lips apart, and she was plunged into a world of alien sensations. Somewhere deep inside of her a flame was being kindled, encouraged by the touch of his hands on her body until it spread like a fire through her veins, awakening a response in her that was clamouring for release beyond the seemingly fragile wall of her resistance.

An eternity seemed to pass before he finally released her and wished her an abrupt 'goodnight', and some time later, as she lay staring into the darkness, she realised to her shame that, although her mind had been relieved, her emotionally awakened body had longed for the moment to continue.

What was happening to her? she wondered frantically. Did the years she had waited around for Andrew starve her to such an extent for a man's kisses that she was prepared to fling herself into the first pair of willing arms? Anna shuddered at the mere thought. She could not deny that she found Scott physically attractive, but then he had the kind of looks and bearing that would make any woman look twice in his direction, and she certainly did not feel any stirrings of love for him – not while her heart still yearned for Andrew.

Desire! The word sprang to the surface of her confused

mind, and she shrank from it mentally. Was that what she had experienced when he had kissed her and caressed her in a way no other man had ever done before?

She groaned and buried her face in her pillow, recalling how she had longed for Andrew's touch and his kisses, but their friendship had never gone beyond the occasional but casual embrace followed by a brotherly peck which had left her totally unsatisfied. Her love for Andrew had been deep and intense, and somehow she had always thought that he had loved her too in his quiet, reserved way. But she had been mistaken, and it had taken Debbie's reappearance on the scene to prove to her how wrong she had been.

There were times, such as this, that she wished she could hurt Andrew as much as he had hurt her, but it was a spiteful wish, she knew, and she realised, too, that it would perhaps be best for her not to see Scott Beresford again unless it was absolutely necessary. Being with him merely awakened thoughts that were uncharitable, and there was, after all, nothing she could do to alter the situation.

The warm climate along the Natal coast attracted tourists from all over the country during the July holidays in order to escape from the cold weather in the other provinces. The Caribbean was filled to capacity and during the next three weeks Anna found that she barely had a moment to spare for herself. During the evenings, when she was free, she found herself wondering occasionally about Scott, and whether he, too, was finding that he had very little time at his disposal, but she usually ended up being annoyed with herself for giving him so much as a thought.

Towards the end of July the tourist trade slackened

considerably when families from the Transvaal returned home to be in time for the re-opening of the schools after the winter holidays, but for Anna it still meant spending hours trying to balance the hotel books, while at the same time attending to guests who came to the reception desk with their requests.

Morris queried an account one morning and, while in the throes of sorting it out, the telephone rang on her desk, making her frown with irritation as she lifted the receiver.

"Caribbean Hotel, good morning."

"That has to be you, Anna," a deep, mocking voice said quite clearly into her ear. "No one else I know of has a voice that reminds me of pure silk."

"Scott!" she sighed impatiently, recognising his voice instantly despite the fact that it was almost three weeks since she had last seen or heard from him. "What do you want?"

"Now, is that a nice way to talk to someone who has taken the trouble to telephone you?" he demanded with a derisive note in his voice.

"I didn't ask you to telephone me," she told him promptly, hating herself for the way her heart was behaving.

"Have you missed me?"

"No!"

"You did think of me, though."

"I never gave you a thought," she lied, ignoring her conscience as it pointed out quite deliberately the occasions when his silence had made her wonder about him.

"How can you say you never gave me a thought after the way I kissed you the last time we –"

"I've got work to do," she interrupted him coldly, not wanting to be reminded of the turmoil her emotions had been in after he had left her that night.

"So have I, so I'll get straight to the point," Scott said abruptly. "You're free this weekend."

"I beg your pardon?"

He laughed softly at the other end and explained. "I've spoken to Morris and you're free from five o'clock Friday afternoon until Sunday evening."

"Really?" she asked coldly, amazed at his audacity.

"Yes, Anna, so pack a bag and be ready at five-thirty, because that's when I'll be there to fetch you."

She drew a careful breath, trying to control the waves of anger that swept over her. "And where, may I ask, am I supposed to be going?"

"You're coming here to Amazibu Bay for the weekend," he informed her arrogantly.

"If you think —"

"Anna, I'm not thinking at the moment, just acting," he interrupted forcefully. "Be ready at five-thirty on Friday . . . or else!"

"Are you threatening me?" she demanded, her fingers tightening on the receiver until her knuckles whitened.

"I would never dream of doing that, my love," he said quite calmly, but the hint of mockery was quite evident in his voice.

"I'm not your . . . love!" she argued hotly.

"You *will* be," he insisted annoyingly and, in a fit of anger, she slammed down the receiver.

Who the devil did he think he was that he could organise her life in this way without even consulting her! she fumed silently, her cheeks flushed with irritation and anger. She did not hear a word from him for three weeks, and then he telephoned and calmly announced that he had made arrangements for her to have the Saturday off, and that she would be spending the weekend at his home. Well, he could just forget about it!

The telephone rang again a few seconds later and as she lifted the receiver, Scott's voice came over the line before she had time to say a word.

"I take it we were cut off, because you would never be ungracious enough to slam the receiver down in some-one's ear, would you?" he remarked caustically, and her anger gave way to helplessness.

"Won't you ever take no for an answer?"

"I haven't asked you yet," he returned swiftly.

Irritated and confused, she said: "Asked me what? What are you talking about?"

"I haven't asked you to marry me yet, so you can't say no," he explained with infuriating calmness, and she drew her breath in sharply.

"I think you must be quite mad!"

His soft laughter barely reached her ears. "Wouldn't it be fun to be mad together?"

Astonishment sparked off a flash of humour and she laughed before she could prevent herself from doing so.

"I wish I was there at this moment," she heard him say, and she controlled herself instantly.

"Why?"

"That's the first time you've laughed, and I wish I could have been there to see you."

A profound silence settled between them while Anna acknowledged silently that he had spoken the truth. It was the first time she had laughed in several months, but then there had been nothing to laugh about until that moment.

"Scott, I really do have work to do," she sighed eventually, glancing at the stack of books and papers littering her desk.

"All right," he agreed abruptly. "See you Friday. Yes?"

"I'll think about it."

"Yes!" he insisted, and Anna could not prevent the smile that curved her lips when she eventually replaced the receiver.

Scott Beresford was really the most impossible man she had ever met, and so very difficult to resist, but she was most certainly going to have a word with Morris for agreeing so readily to Scott's suggestions.

Her opportunity arrived when Morris came to enquire later that morning how she was progressing with the account he had asked her to check.

"I believe Scott Beresford telephoned you," she began, watching his reaction closely.

"Yes, and I agreed that you could have this Saturday off," Morris replied smoothly. "You've worked very hard these past weeks."

"You could have asked me first before agreeing to give me time off," she rebuked him slightly.

"I thought you'd be glad to get away for a few days," he exclaimed in surprise.

"But not with Scott Beresford," she protested.

Morris's dark glance sharpened. "I couldn't very well refuse the man who pays my salary, and besides, I thought you liked him?"

"I . . ." Her denial died on her lips and, to her dismay, she realised that she could not admit truthfully to disliking Scott. He was arrogant and insufferable most times, but, so far, she had not found herself bored in his company. Pulling herself together, she met Morris's level gaze. "You really had no right to say yes on my behalf, Morris."

"I never did that," he denied instantly. "I merely

agreed that you could have Saturday morning off, and the rest was up to you." He sat down on the corner of her desk and regarded her closely for a moment. "I suppose you refused his invitation?"

Anna looked away uncomfortably. "As a matter of fact, I didn't. I accepted."

"Then what are you fussing about?" he demanded, gesturing exasperatedly.

"I was more or less forced into it," she explained irritably.

"Hm ... he's a man after my own heart. Forceful and determined." Morris grinned at her mischievously. "He's the kind of man most women need, or they end up wearing the trousers instead of the man."

He chuckled to himself as he strode across the foyer and entered his office, leaving Anna with the realisation that it was typical of him to condone Scott's behaviour. Morris, when he wished, could be just as forceful and determined once he had made up his mind about something, and nothing would sway him from the decision he had made.

Anna was still up in her room the Friday afternoon Scott was supposed to call for her when there was a sharp tap on her door. Thinking it would be Sheila, she called, "Come in."

"Count Dracula at your service," Scott announced himself, bowing slightly as she swung round to face him in surprise.

"You're an idiot," she rebuked him, a hint of laughter in her voice as she saw him straighten and walk towards her with an unfathomable expression in his eyes.

"You're quite right," he admitted. "I've become an idiot over you."

His presence in her bedroom was disturbing, and his

nearness stirred her senses until she was potently aware
of his long, muscular legs clad in pale grey slacks, and
the width of his shoulders in the perfectly tailored blue
jacket. She had hoped that, after not seeing him for
three weeks, she would find the effect he had had on her
would have worn off, but it had instead increased alarm-
ingly.

"I wish you wouldn't say things like that," she said
angrily, turning away to pick up her jacket which she
had placed in readiness on the bed.

"Does it embarrass you?" he mocked her, and she
turned to face him then with a look of pleading in her
eyes.

"I'm being serious, Scott."

"So am I," he said quietly, his steady glance capturing
hers for several seconds before he gestured towards the
small suitcase at the foot of her bed. "Is this what you're
taking with you?"

"Yes," she nodded, draping her jacket across her arm
and picking up her handbag.

"Let's go, then."

The silence was a little disturbing between them as
they went down in the elevator and crossed the pannelled
foyer with its potted ferns. It was not until they had left
the city behind hem, taking the coastal road to Amazibu
Bay, that Anna ventured to speak for the first time.

"Won't your aunt think it strange, my coming to
Amazibu Bay, I mean?"

"Aunt Dorrie?" he questioned, glancing at her swiftly.
"Not at all. She knows all about you and is dying to
meet you."

"Do you make a practice of inviting women to your
home for the weekend?" she asked, wondering cynically
whether his aunt had begun to take this sort of thing in

her stride.

"Only if they have red hair and green eyes, yes," he mocked her.

"Be serious!"

"Would you believe me if I told you you're the first woman I've ever taken to my home to meet my aunt since – well, since my wife died?"

She stared at him for a moment, but as the darkness settled about them she was unable to see his expression in the faint light of the dashboard, but his voice conveyed a sincerity that was unmistakable.

"I believe you," she said after a moment and, to her surprise, his hand left the steering wheel and found hers in her lap. The pressure of his fingers was brief before he returned his hand to the wheel, but Anna became aware of that strange tingling sensation winding its way through her body.

To her disappointment she saw very little of Amazibu Bay, for they arrived there after dark, but his home, situated virtually on the beach as he had once explained, was large and imposing, with a row of marble pillars along the length of the terrace. Scott ushered her into the spacious hall, and she barely had time to glimpse the heavy crystal chandeliers hanging from the high ceiling before she noticed the slender, grey-haired woman approaching them. Her hair was short and perfectly styled, and the eyes were a deep blue like Scott's, but there the likeness ended, for her face was fuller, and the welcoming smile held a warmth untainted by mockery.

"Aunt Dorrie, I would like you to meet Anna Lindsay," Scott introduced them, touching Anna's arm and propelling her forward slightly. "Anna, this is my aunt, Dorothy MacPherson."

A well-kept hand gripped Anna's. "My dear, I've

heard so much about you, but I can see now why Scott hasn't been able to talk of anything else lately."

"Can you blame me, Aunt Dorrie?"

"Now that I've met her?" Dorothy MacPherson questioned in her well-modulated voice as she released Anna's hand and stood back a little to appraise her. Then she shook her head. "No, I can't really blame you, dear boy."

"Should I be blushing?" Anna demanded a little coldly, feeling very much like an animal on display.

"You must think us terribly rude, Anna. Here we are talking about you as if you weren't here," the older woman smiled apologetically, linking her arm through Anna's. "Come, let me show you to your room before we have dinner."

Scott touched Anna's arm and pressed her suitcase into her hand. "Don't stay away too long," he warned softly.

"Go through to the living-room and pour yourself something to drink. It will keep you occupied until we join you," his aunt told him firmly as she led Anna up the carpeted stairs with the ornately carved balustrade.

Anna followed her along a short passage which led off into yet another before they entered a large bedroom which overlooked the sea and a large section of the coast-line, and she glanced about her appreciatively, taking in the deep blue and white of the furnishings.

"I hope you'll find the room comfortable," Dorothy MacPherson remarked beside her, indicating the door leading off the bedroom. "You'll find the bathroom through there."

Anna smiled, placing her suitcase at the foot of the bed. "This looks cool and beautiful, and I hope my coming here hasn't inconvenienced you in any way."

"Of course not, my dear," Scott's aunt replied, glancing about the room critically before she added, "Scott seldom invites people to stay these days, and it's such a pity when one thinks of this large house standing virtually empty."

Anna was tempted to question her about Scott's marriage, but she decided against it and asked instead, "Don't you find it lonely?"

"I did, at first, until I got used to Scott always being away somewhere on business," his aunt admitted. "But I'm hoping things will change soon."

When Anna stared at her blankly she added hastily, "We'd better go downstairs and not keep Scott waiting much longer."

"Ah, at last!" Scott sighed as they entered the spaciously modern living-room with its padded, cream-coloured chairs, cool green curtains, and strategically placed Grecian marble statuettes. "A sherry, Anna? Aunt Dorrie?"

"Not at the moment, Scott," his aunt declined hastily. "I still have a few things to do before I can join you for dinner."

She excused herself and Anna was suddenly left alone with Scott while he poured sherry into two delicately stemmed glasses and joined her on the sofa. He touched the rim of his glass to hers, and their glances locked for timeless seconds as they raised their glasses to their lips. The look in his eyes reminded her of that first time she had looked up during the seminar to find him observing her and, just as she did then, she found it disconcerting, and once again it was she who had to look away.

"I presume you were kept busy over these past weeks?" he asked casually, and she sighed inwardly with relief as the awkward moment passed.

"I was kept busy, yes, but now that the rush is over I find myself saddled with piles of paper work."

"Do you enjoy your work?" he continued to question her.

"If I didn't enjoy it I wouldn't have stayed on longer than a month," she assured him coldly.

"Then I'm glad you decided to stay on, or I might never have met you."

She glanced at him sharply. "It would perhaps have been better if we'd never met at all."

His heavy eyebrows rose a fraction, but he drained his glass calmly and placed it on the small glass table beside him before turning to face her with the usual hint of mockery in his eyes.

"Did you miss me at all these past weeks?"

"Should I have?" she asked guardedly, running the tip of her finger along the rim of her glass.

"Admit that you thought of me occasionally."

His deep voice was very persuasive, and she took the last mouthful of her sherry to give her the courage she needed before replying, "Very occasionally, yes."

"Good, then we're getting somewhere at last," he sighed, removing the empty glass from her fingers and placing it on the table beside his own.

"Are we supposed to be getting somewhere?" she asked a little mockingly.

"Most definitely," he insisted firmly as he shifted closer to her. "Tell me, when you thought of me, did you remember my kisses?"

Her breath locked in her throat, but the anger flaring sharply within her was directed at herself, and not at him. She *had* remembered his kisses whenever she had thought of him; she had recalled them only too vividly, as well as every abominable sensation which had been aroused by them.

"Scott, if you're trying to make me hate you, then you're going about it in the right way," she said at last, her voice as cold and distant as she could make it.

"I would prefer your hatred to your indifference, my love."

"I'm not —" She bit off the rest of her sentence, horrified at herself for almost admitting that she was not indifferent to this man seated beside her with his muscular thigh almost touching her own.

"Yes?" he prompted with a hint of mockery in his eyes as he allowed his glance to linger on the agitated rise and fall of her small, firm breasts.

"Nothing!" she snapped irritably.

"You were either going to say that you're *not* indifferent to me, or that you're *not* my love." The sound of his soft laughter shivered along her receptive nerves. "The tantalising question is, which one was it going to be?"

Avoiding his probing glance, she said untruthfully, "I was going to say that I'm not interested in your preferences."

"She speaks poniards, and every word stabs."

"Quoting Shakespeare won't help you either," she snapped, flashing him an angry glance, but he caught her chin roughly between his fingers and forced her to meet his eyes.

"You're not only beautiful, but you're clever too."

"We did *Much Ado About Nothing* in high school."

His lips twisted sardonically. "Did you take the part of Beatrice, by any chance?"

Realising that he thought her as sharp-tongued as Shakespeare's heroine, she said coldly, "No, I helped with the production of the play."

"Pity," he drawled mockingly. "You would have been an excellent Beatrice."

"I shall ignore that remark," she said abruptly, brushing aside the hand that gripped her chin and rising to her feet just as Dorothy MacPherson entered the living-room.

"Dinner is served, children," she smiled at them, and both Scott and Anna managed to give the impression that nothing had occurred to upset the tranquil atmosphere which had existed on their arrival.

CHAPTER THREE

ANNA'S mood mellowed during dinner, and Dorothy MacPherson's warmth and friendliness helped considerably to ease the inexplicable tension which had sprung up between Scott and herself. Anna was made to feel at ease and was drawn into the conversation quite naturally as if she were an old acquaintance of the family.

It reminded Anna of the many occasions when Andrew had dined at her parents' home in Johannesburg. Her parents had liked him from the moment they had met him, and Andrew had become a part of their family circle as if he had always belonged.

"Have you ever walked on the beach in the moonlight?" Scott interrupted her painful thoughts, and she shook herself free of them to glance at him across the table.

"No, I haven't."

"Then fetch something to throw over your shoulders, and I'll introduce you to a sight you've never seen before," he instructed, pushing back his chair and getting to his feet.

"Don't stay out too late," his aunt warned when Anna came downstairs a few minutes later with a cardigan draped across her shoulders. "It gets chilly in the evenings."

"Don't worry, Aunt Dorrie," Scott smiled humorously, placing his arm about Anna's waist with an easy familiarity and drawing her firmly against his side. "She'll have me to keep her warm."

"Scott!" his aunt exclaimed, her reproving glance tainted with faint humour as she transferred her gaze to Anna who stood rigidly beside her nephew. "Don't take any notice of him, Anna."

"I'm beginning to think I should decline your offer, Scott," Anna remarked with forced casualness, moving beyond the circle of his arm as she glanced up at him.

"I promise to behave myself," he mocked her as he gripped her hand and drew her towards the door. "Come on."

They left the house and strolled down the avenue of palms towards the large gate through which they had entered that evening. The air was cool and scented with the tanginess of the sea on that cloudless night with the stars adding a certain brilliance to the sky. Scott took Anna's arm as they crossed the road and climbed down the steps leading on to the beach and, although the sand was firm beneath her feet, she was glad that she had exchanged her shoes for a pair of low-heeled sandals.

"It's been three weeks since I last saw you, and I had to get you to myself for a while," Scott broke the uncomfortable silence between them, and Anna sent a mocking glance in his direction as they walked along the shore with the waves breaking close to their feet.

"I thought you wanted me to experience the thrill of walking on the beach in the moonlight."

"Take a look at that," he said abruptly, gripping her shoulders and turning her to face the sea as it lay shimmering in the silvery glow of the full moon. "Could anyone wish for a more romantic setting?"

She stiffened instantly. "I'm not looking for romance."

"Don't disappoint me, Anna," he mocked her as they continued their walk along the now deserted stretch of beach. "Every woman yearns for romance, and you're no different from the rest."

Warning signals flashed through her mind, and she frowned. "Scott, whatever it is you have in mind, I must warn you again that you're wasting your time."

"You're not going to tell me there's someone else," he accused sharply, guiding her towards a wooden bench a little further up the beach.

"There was someone — once," she admitted reluctantly, aware of his warm hand beneath her elbow even as Andrew Tait's handsome features were projected on the screen of her memory.

"How long ago?" Scott persisted.

"Seven months, to be exact."

"What happened?"

"You wouldn't want me to bore you with the details," she evaded his question as they sat down on the bench, facing the restless sea.

"I *want* to know the details," Scott insisted, lighting a cigarette and stretching his long legs out before him.

Loath to discuss a subject which still caused her a considerable amount of pain, she searched fruitlessly for some way to avoid it, but Scott's penetrating glance in the moonlit darkness finally forced her to plunge into an abrupt explanation.

"I was in love with – with someone, and for five years we had a sort of understanding which I imagined would one day lead to marriage. He was working his way through university, and I was prepared to wait."

"That was rather foolish, wasn't it? Wasting your life away like that?" Scott questioned abruptly, drawing hard on his cigarette until the tip glowed a bright red in the darkness.

"I suppose so, but I loved him and I was prepared to wait an eternity, if necessary," she replied a little defiantly.

"You loved him that much?"

His voice sounded a little incredulous and Anna glanced at him sharply. "Yes, I loved him that much."

"What made you give up in the end?"

She looked away then, out across the sea to where the ocean lay shimmering like a living, breathing thing in the moonlight. "My young sister Debbie grew up in the meantime, and he decided he preferred her. They were married three months ago."

"So the years you waited around were all for nothing," he remarked quietly, the aroma of tobacco mingling with the freshness of the air.

His statement of fact stabbed cruelly at her heart, and she whispered reluctantly, "Yes, it was all for nothing."

Scott pushed the remainder of his cigarette into the sand at his feet and turned to face her, his arm sliding along the back of the bench behind her shoulders. "Are you planning to spend the rest of your life pining for someone you can't have?"

"Pining?" she echoed a little stupidly.

"Yes, pining," he repeated harshly. "Time doesn't stand still, Anna, not even for someone as lovely as you, and there are other men who could make you just as happy, if not happier than he could have done."

"*You*, for instance?" she asked cynically.

"Why not?"

She tensed inwardly. "Is this a proposal, Scott?"

"You must admit that the setting is right," he laughed softly, but there was a dangerous quality in his voice that made her change the subject quickly.

"You haven't told me much about yourself."

"That's because there isn't much to tell," he replied with that hint of harshness still in his voice. "I married Trudie four years ago. She died two years later in a car accident."

Regretting that she had mentioned the subject, she murmured apologetically, "I'm sorry."

He fingered the silk of her hair where it lay across her shoulder. "If I wasn't free now I wouldn't have been able to ask you to marry me."

"You're not serious, Scott," she rebuked him quietly.

"I'm very serious."

"But you hardly know me," she protested, odd sensations shivering along her nerves as his warm fingers caressed the nape of her neck.

"We've known each other for almost five weeks."

"During which we've seen each other exactly three times," she reminded him swiftly.

"You're not counting the other occasions when we saw each other in passing at the Caribbean."

"Scott, you're suggesting the impossible," she argued, attempting to move away from him, but his hand shifted to her shoulder and prevented her from doing so.

"Tell me you'll at least think it over," he insisted, his breath warm against her temple.

"It won't do any good," she assured him, firmly convinced that no one could ever take Andrew's place in her heart, but Scott was equally determined as he tipped her face up to his.

"Anna, I'm not asking you to marry me immediately, but you might as well know what I have in mind. I intend to do everything within my power to make you say yes."

"You'll be disappointed."

"I don't think so." His voice was vibrantly low, and it washed over her like a caress that quickened her pulse and awakened a hungry yearning deep inside of her. "You're going to be mine, Anna. And soon," he added.

The moon and stars were obscured from her vision as his mouth descended on hers, and nothing else seemed to matter beyond the strength of his arms about her and the pressure of his lips as they coaxed a response from hers. She knew she had to resist, but found that she couldn't, and she finally yielded beneath the storm of emotions as it washed over her.

"Scott, this is madness," she pleaded eventually.

"Crazy, wonderful madness," he agreed, his lips sliding along the sensitive cord of her neck and lingering against the hollow at the base of her throat.

She could feel her pulse throbbing wildly against his burning lips and, frightened by it, she gasped, "We should go back to the house."

"Not yet."

"Scott —"

"You talk too much," he interrupted hoarsely, his arms tightening about her as his lips found hers again.

His sensuous mouth and caressing hands awakened emotions which sharpened on desire, and she trembled, pressing closer to him without actually realising what she was doing and sliding her hand over his smooth dark head, allowing it to linger at the nape of his strong neck where the hair was short and springy to the touch. She felt quite lightheaded with the force of her emotions when they finally drew apart, and she was suddenly frightened by the intensity of the feelings she had not known she possessed until that moment.

"I always suspected that beneath that cool exterior there lurked a passionate soul, and now I'm convinced," Scott laughed softly, the sound of his voice bringing her back to earth with a speed that was sickening, and her anger flared at the realisation that he had found her weakness amusing.

"Let me go!" she cried chokingly, escaping from his arms and jumping to her feet.

Her action had caught him unawares, but he appeared quite unperturbed as he followed her example and stood towering over her on the quiet beach with only the sound of the surf to disturb the peace.

"It's too late, my love, I've discovered your secret," he murmured softly, his eyes glinting strangely in the moonlight.

"You're insufferable!" she gasped, her breath coming agitatedly over her parted lips.

"And you're beautiful, standing there looking so deceptively cold and aloof in the moonlight," he mocked her without hesitation, succeeding in fanning her anger further.

"I'm taking the first train back to Durban tomorrow morning," she voiced her decision sharply.

"Just think of what you would be missing if you should decide to go," he taunted her relentlessly.

"I shan't miss anything of value," she snapped, her back rigid and her nerves taut.

"You'll miss my kisses."

Anna flinched as if he had struck her and clenched her hands at her sides. He was really an insensitive brute, and she cringed inwardly with shame as she recalled the way she had responded to his lovemaking. "Your arrogance astounds me," she managed eventually in a cold, shaky voice.

"The truth is often mistaken for arrogance," he hit back without hesitation, and she swung away from him angrily, intending to walk back the way they had come, but Scott's hand latched on to her arm, jerking her roughly against him. "Where do you think you're going?"

"Back to the house before I lose my temper completely," she said through clenched teeth while she tried to free her arm.

"You're not going anywhere ... yet," he said harshly. His hand tightened painfully on her arm as her struggles increased, and tears of frustration and anger filled her eyes as she finally gasped, "You're hurting me!"

"Stop fighting me, Anna," he instructed calmly, his grip slackening but not releasing her. "Let's rather make use of the time we have together by getting to know each other instead of sparring verbally in this manner."

His fingers caressed her arm where moments ago he had bruised her soft flesh, and she tried to ignore the deliciously tingling sensation it aroused as she stared up at him and tried to read his expression in the darkness.

"Are you suggesting that we call a truce?"

"I am." He released her then and extended his right hand towards her. "Do we shake on it?"

Her anger subsided as swiftly as it had risen, and she sighed as she placed her hand in his. "You're really the most impossible man I've ever met, but – yes, let's call a truce."

"Are you still going to rush back to Durban on the early morning train?" he asked softly, raising her hand to his lips and surprising her by kissing each finger in turn.

"No," she shook her head, swallowing down the peculiar tightness in her throat.

"Good girl!"

They strolled back to the house with his arm draped casually about her shoulders, and she found herself wondering whether he had, in fact, been serious when he had suggested marriage. It was too ridiculous even to contemplate, and yet ... there was something about him that attracted her against her will, despite the many times he had succeeded in angering her.

"How long has your aunt been staying with you?" she finally asked as they walked through the gates, keeping to the shadows of the palm trees.

"Ever since her husband died five years ago."

"Is she your father's sister?"

"My mother's."

"Are your parents –?"

"They died some years ago," he said abruptly. "My father died of a thrombosis, and my mother just lost the will to live."

"I'm sorry."

Scott did not comment, but his arm tightened slightly about her as they walked up the steps and entered the house. His aunt had coffee waiting for them and remained to chat for a few minutes before she tactfully retired, but Anna had no intention of being left alone with Scott.

"It's been a long day," she said, getting to her feet, and Scott followed suit to accompany her to her room, but when she was about to enter it his hands on her shoulders detained her.

"I meant every word when I asked you to consider marrying me," he said sternly as if he was aware of the fact that she had not taken him quite seriously, and she lowered her eyes before the intensity of his gaze.

"I'm beginning to realise that, yes."

"And?"

She felt like a hunted animal being driven into a corner, and she tensed inwardly. "You must give me time to think about it."

"How much time do you need?"

"Don't rush me, Scott," she pleaded, her mind searching frantically for escape from this situation which was becoming increasingly difficult for her to handle.

"Two weeks?" he persisted relentlessly.

"Very well," she sighed, accepting this momentary reprieve. "Two weeks."

His lips twisted cynically as he observed her expression of relief. "I'm not going to stay away from you during those two weeks, if that's what you were hoping for."

"I never imagined you would," she retorted, a reluctant smile plucking at the corners of her mouth.

There was no answering smile on his lips as he lowered his head and kissed her long and hard on the mouth. It was a slightly punishing kiss, but it still had the power to make her feel weak in the knees and, when he released her, she stood swaying slightly, her heart drumming heavily against her temples.

"Sleep well, my love," he murmured in a slightly mocking tone of voice, and the next moment she was alone with her confused and bewildered thoughts.

Scott *was* serious about marrying her, and she would have to give it equally serious thought, but, with Andrew's image still so painfully vivid in her heart and mind, how was she going to be able to contemplate marriage to someone else?

"Oh, Lord," she moaned, burying her face in her hands once she was in the seclusion of her room. "Why couldn't Andrew have loved me the way I loved him, then none of this would have been necessary."

There was no answer to this gnawing problem and she shelved it eventually, sighing with irritation as she prepared herself for going to bed.

From force of habit Anna awoke early the following morning and, throwing open the windows, she stared out across the spacious garden with its palms, well-kept lawns, and sub-tropical shrubs. A flash of white caught her eye and, dressing hastily, she went down to join Dorothy MacPherson on her stroll through the garden.

"This is the best time of the day," Mrs. MacPherson smiled at Anna from beneath her wide sun-hat. "Everything still seems so fresh in the early morning sunlight."

"I never realised you had such a beautiful garden," Anna said, glancing about her appreciatively as she fell into step beside the older woman. "Do you do the gardening yourself, or do you have someone to help you?"

"With a garden this size we can't do without a gardener, but I enjoy pottering about in the soil when I get the opportunity."

'This is paradise,' Anna thought as she stared up at the whitewashed mansion with its marble pillars. With the sound of the sea in her ears as they walked beneath the palm trees she could almost believe that this was an oasis in the desert. The high walls about the grounds offered seclusion and privacy from the neighbours, and privacy was, no doubt, something which Scott needed at times.

Scott! She had almost forgotten about him, and turning to the woman walking beside her, she asked, "Is Scott still asleep?"

"Good heavens, no," his aunt laughed briefly. "Scott always comes down very early in the mornings. He's most probably in his study at this moment, wading through a pile of paper work, and quite unaware that you're such an early riser as well." She glanced at the large dial on her wristwatch. "It's time we had breakfast. Would you like to go through to Scott's study and ask him to join us in the breakfast-room?"

Curious to see a little more of the house, and not so much Scott himself, Anna agreed, and following the directions Mrs. MacPherson had given her she hurried through the hall and down the passage on the right, but her heart pounded uncomfortably when she hesitated outside the closed door of what she knew to be his study.

She knocked tentatively, and as his deep voice barked an abrupt "Come in", she took a deep breath and entered his private sanctum.

Scott's eyebrows rose sharply and, pushing aside his work, he got to his feet. "This is a pleasant surprise," he smiled briefly, his warm, appreciative glance sliding from her red-gold hair down to her sandalled feet before meeting her unwavering green eyes. "I thought you would still be asleep."

"I've been walking in your lovely garden with your aunt," she informed him a little tritely because of her efforts to control her wayward pulses. "She suggested that I should ask you to join us for breakfast."

"That was a very good suggestion," he agreed softly, coming towards her with a wicked gleam in his blue eyes. "Now I can say good morning to you without a curious audience."

Her breath locked in her throat as she backed away from him swiftly, but Scott's long legs bridged the gap with ease and she was swept into an embrace that crushed her soft slenderness against the hard length of him. His fiery kisses seared through her until every nerve in her treacherous body was vibrantly alive to the sheer maleness of him, and all thoughts of resistance fled when his hands slid caressingly down her back to linger possessively against her hips. She was flushed and trembling when he finally raised his head, and she began to struggle against him in a futile attempt to place some distance between them.

"Don't you think it's a little early in the morning for this sort of thing?" she demanded, flashing him an angry glance.

"It's never too early," he contradicted smoothly, his eyes mocking her and lingering on her throbbing lips. "You're so beautiful that I find you hard to resist, my ice princess."

"I would appreciate it if you'd let me go so we could go and have our breakfast. Your aunt is waiting for us," she announced, attempting to keep her voice cool and despising herself for its shakiness.

His hold on her slackened and making use of the opportunity she twisted free of his arms. She was across the room and had opened the door before he could prevent her, but she knew there was mockery in his eyes as he walked silently beside her through the house.

She would feel much safer when they had joined his aunt, she thought, quickening her pace as they approached the breakfast-room. Scott was dangerously attractive in his black rollnecked sweater and tight-fitting hipsters, she decided, and her senses were too vitally aware of him as a man at that moment; a man whose magnetism she was finding extraordinarily difficult to resist.

It was at the breakfast table that Scott announced his intention to take Anna out for the day, and although she experienced a flicker of panic at the onset, she soon found herself relaxing and enjoying his company. He introduced her to Amazibu Bay with its tree-lined streets, its old-fashioned shops with gaily coloured awnings, and the vast new shopping complex which had been opened only recently. A modern theatre, cinemas, restaurants and night-clubs had also been erected, as well as a large playground on the beach-front which catered to young and old. They had lunch at an open-air restaurant, and finally ended up strolling along the banks of the river to admire the waterlilies which grew so abundantly in the water close to the edge.

"Amazibu Bay relies a great deal on its tourist trade," Scott explained. "It's not a very large town, as you can see, and it's very quiet out of season."

"According to Morris and Sheila, from December to February are the busiest months." Her glance was questioning as she raised it to his. "Do you find it so as well?"

"Undoubtedly," he nodded briefly, drawing her down beside him on to the soft grass beneath a shady tree. "Amazibu Bay is inundated with tourists during the summer months. That's when I close up the house and spend a few weeks at my beach cottage in the Cape. Aunt Dorrie usually spends the Christmas season with her daughter in Cape Town, and then we return just after New Year."

Anna tugged at a blade of grass and twisted it lazily about her finger. "Do you have a secretary to do your personal correspondence?"

"Not at the moment. I usually have a problem finding someone suitable, and lately I've been borrowing a secretary at one of the hotels," he admitted, lying down on his back and locking his hands behind his head as he stared up at the cloudless sky through the branches of the tree.

"What would you require this person to do?"

"I need someone to help me with the paper work – the books, the accounts, the typing, and so forth."

"I see," she murmured, trying to think of someone whom she could recommend.

"If you marry me then *you* could help me instead of someone else," Scott told her teasingly, and the blade of grass snapped between her agitated fingers.

"You're just on the look-out for cheap labour, Scott Beresford," she accused him sharply.

"You'll benefit, naturally, by having me as your husband," he continued lazily with a hint of mockery in his glance.

"You think a lot of yourself, don't you?" she asked disdainfully, but her pulse quickened as he sat up beside her and fingered a curl behind her ear.

"A husband could be a far more rewarding pay packet than paper notes and jingling coins in your purse," he insisted, his shoulder touching hers and sending a tremor of awareness through her.

Her eyes flashed with anger, but she had the crazy desire to laugh as she said: "This is strictly your opinion, of course?"

"Of course."

The devilish gleam in his eyes warned her that the situation was becoming dangerous, but his hands gripped her shoulders and pushed her firmly down on to the soft grass before she had time to escape him.

"Scott, please!" she begged, her hands against his broad chest where she could feel the heavy, rhythmic thudding of his heart through the thin silk sweater, but he paid no attention to her pleas and she found herself trapped beneath his weight with his sensuous mouth just above her own. There was no mistaking his intentions, and she struggled against him in a fit of panic. "Someone might see us," she protested helplessly.

"I don't mind if they do," he laughed softly, his breath warm against her mouth, and then the world exploded about her as his lips took possession of hers.

She knew only too well that it was futile to fight against the emotions he was so successfully arousing, and she relaxed against him for a time until a spark of sanity made her wrench her mouth from his.

"That's enough – please!" she pleaded, her voice shaky and unfamiliar to her own ears as she looked up at him with eyes that were no longer cold and distant, but misty and bemused as a result of his kisses.

Scott shook his head slightly, a cynical little smile playing about his lips as he released her and stood up, drawing her to her feet at the same time. "It's not nearly enough but, for the time being, I agree with you."

His hands at her waist seemed to burn through the thin material of her dress and, for one frightening second, she had the mad desire to fling herself back into his arms, but she pulled herself together sharply as they walked back to where he had parked his Mercedes.

At the local night-club that evening Scott drew her on to the dance floor and remarked wryly, "It's one way of holding you in my arms without causing a stir."

Anna found it difficult to hide the smile that plucked at her lips, and she relaxed, giving up the effort to analyse the effect he had on her. There was no earthly reason why she should not enjoy his company, and one very important reason why she should encourage a less antagonistic relationship with him. He had asked her to marry him and during the next two weeks she would have to give it serious consideration. She was no longer a child; she was twenty-five, and after wasting five years of her youth she could not afford to waste much more.

If Scott noticed the change in her attitude towards him, then he gave no indication of it, but later that evening, when he kissed her goodnight outside her bedroom door, he looked almost infuriatingly triumphant when she surrendered to his embrace without protest. It was the first time she had actually given him her lips willingly, and the effect on Scott was totally devastating. He swept her into a fierce embrace, subjecting her to a barrage of passionate kisses which left her weak and breathless for some time afterwards, and she fell asleep that night with a smile on her lips which she could not even begin to explain to herself.

When Scott drove her back to Durban after dinner the following evening, she felt a twinge of regret that the weekend had passed so quickly. It had been a delightful change getting away from the city and, on Dorothy Mac-Pherson's insistence, they had spent the Sunday lounging in the garden, or strolling on the beach. There had been times when they had been silent, but it had not been an uncomfortable silence, and she had experienced a new tranquillity when they had relaxed in their chairs, watching the slow progress of the fleecy clouds as they drifted across the deep blue sky.

Anna's thoughts were jerked back to the present when Scott finally parked his car beneath the shadows of the trees close to the entrance of the Caribbean. Her hand fluttered towards the handle, but it was instantly caught in his firm clasp.

"You will think very seriously about marrying me,

won't you?"

His face was a dark, expressionless shadow as she looked up at him searchingly. "I promise to give it very serious thought, but I –"

"No buts," he interrupted harshly. "I want an answer in two weeks' time, and the answer must be yes."

He moved then with unexpected swiftness, and she found herself caught against him with her head thrown back over his arm. His hard mouth found hers without much difficulty in the shadowy darkness, and she no longer had the desire to think as she yielded to the passionate demand of his lips and hands.

It was some time before she managed to disengage herself and when she stepped out of the car on to the tarred driveway she found that her legs were trembling. Scott's soft laughter mocked her and she avoided his eyes angrily as he escorted her through the plush foyer and into the elevator. Neither of them spoke until they reached the third floor, but outside her bedroom door she turned to face him, her expression cool and controlled.

"It's been a lovely weekend, Scott, and I must thank you and your aunt for making it so."

He raised her hands to his lips, but his eyes never left hers, and their probing intensity unnerved her as they always did. It was impossible to remain cool and aloof with Scott, for he penetrated her defences each time with uncanny ease. Their relationship had progressed further than she had intended it to, but even at that moment, as his hands moved to her shoulders with a touch of possessiveness to draw her closer, she found herself raising her lips for his kiss with a hungry yearning which was becoming increasingly humiliating. The mocking little smile hovering about his mouth somehow no longer troubled her, and she closed her eyes, her lips parting beneath his of their own volition. His hands seemed to burn her through the thin silkiness of her dress as they slid down her back, moulding her body against the muscular hardness of his, and her pulse quickened as intoxicating sensations leapt through her veins like fire.

"Goodnight, my love," he said at length, his arms falling away from her, and she leaned back weakly against her door as she watched him walk towards the elevator with those lithe strides she was beginning to know so well.

Her glance lingered dreamily on the broad, formidable back which tapered down to slim hips, and she suppressed with difficulty the crazy desire to call him back to her. As the elevator doors closed behind him, she came to her senses and, angered and confused at her irrational thoughts, she unlocked her door and carried her suitcase inside. The spell he had cast over her no longer existed, and she would not become a victim of it again.

That was what she decided, but an outrageous little voice deep inside her spoke words to the contrary, and the battle of making up her mind about Scott Beresford began with a vengeance.

CHAPTER FOUR

DURING the next two weeks Anna was not allowed to forget the fact that Scott had asked her to marry him. He showered her with flowers and expensive gifts until it became almost embarrassing, and an evening seldom passed without him putting in an appearance at the Caribbean and taking her out somewhere. She was becoming accustomed to witnessing the knowing glances which passed between Morris and Sheila, and she hated herself for not being able to confide in them.

Despite all her inner protestations, Anna began to look forward to the evenings when she would see Scott, and she felt depressed and listless when he stayed away for some reason. The temptation to telephone him on such occasions was very strong, but the thought of his mockery prevented her from doing so. This did not prevent her from wondering what he was doing, however, and she wondered whether he, too, was thinking of her. It was a maddening situation, but she found she no longer had complete control over her thoughts.

It was on one such an evening that she succumbed to the invitation to have tea with Sheila in their private suite, and her association with Scott was inevitably discussed.

"You've been seeing Scott Beresford quite regularly," Sheila broached the subject tentatively. "I hope you haven't taken him seriously?"

Anna stared down at her hands which were folded so tightly in her lap, and frowned. "Scott has asked me to marry him."

A stunned silence followed her statement before Sheila said: "It seems as though I've been wrong about him, but I never imagined he'd stop playing the field and settle down to marriage again." She paused briefly, her glance speculative. "Have you accepted?"

"I said I would think about it, and he expects an answer by the end of this week."

"And what have you decided?"

Anna shrugged helplessly and rose to her feet all in one graceful movement to pace the floor restlessly. "I haven't decided anything ... yet."

"Do you love him?"

Anna glanced sharply at Sheila. "I loved Andrew, and where did that lead me?"

"What are your feelings towards Scott Beresford, then?" Sheila asked quietly, and Anna turned away to stare out of the window down to where the coloured lights were swaying in the breeze along the beach-front.

"I don't know what I really feel," she admitted after a thoughtful silence. "I don't deny that I find him attractive and enjoy his company, but ..."

"You don't love him," Sheila filled in for her, and Anna's green eyes darkened as unhappy memories returned to haunt her.

"I don't think I could love anyone again the way I once loved Andrew. What I have to offer now is second best, and I'm not sure whether Scott would be satisfied with that."

"Does he know about Andrew?"

"Yes."

"And he still wants to marry you?"

"Yes."

"Then you don't really have to worry on that score, do you?" Sheila observed calmly.

"I know, but ..." Anna sighed and returned to her chair. 'The problem is, what if I agree to marry him and the marriage doesn't work out?"

"That's a chance we all take," Sheila assured her confidently. "But I'm afraid the decision rests with you entirely."

"I know," Anna replied despondently.

"One thing you should remember, though," Sheila added firmly. "You're not getting any younger, and at the age of twenty-five it isn't always easy to find the right man."

Sheila's remark remained with Anna during the remainder of that week. *The right man*, Sheila had said, but was Scott the right man?

Anna was still not certain of this when Scott fetched her at the Caribbean on Saturday afternoon and drove her out to Amazibu Bay to spend the weekend at his home. Some time during the weekend Scott would expect an answer from her, and the knowledge that she had still not made up her mind left her tense and unresponsive in his company. The subject was not mentioned between them, but each time his glance met hers she knew it was just as much on the surface of his thoughts as it was on hers, and it filled her with an uneasiness that made her wish that there was some way she could escape the entire situation.

After dinner that evening she knew somehow that the inevitable could no longer be avoided, and she tensed inwardly when Scott took her through to his study and closed the door firmly behind them. This was the moment she had dreaded, and Scott's resolute expression spoke volumes as he walked across to his desk and opened a drawer.

"I have something here for you," he said, coming towards her with a small, velvet-covered box in his hand. He flicked it open and she felt as though someone had driven their fist into her stomach when she found herself staring at the large solitaire diamond ring nestling against the satin cushion.

It sparkled as though it were alive, mocking her as she recalled how she had dreamed of Andrew one day placing a ring on her finger, but it was on Debbie's finger he had eventually placed his ring.

"It's an engagement ring," she said stupidly, fighting against the waves of pain which threatened to engulf her.

"What else?" Scott demanded with a sardonic expression on his lean face as he moved the small box from side to side, and the stone flashed brilliantly as it was caught in the light of the desk lamp.

Anna wrenched her hypnotic glance from the ring and glanced up at Scott with a suspicion of fear in her eyes. "I haven't said I'd marry you."

"But you're going to give me the answer I've been hoping for."

His presumptuous statement brought her sharply to her senses and whipped up her anger. "You seem very sure of that?"

"I am."

"Marriage is a very serious undertaking," she reminded him coldly, but as he came towards her a wave of helplessness swept over her.

"I know all about marriage being a serious business," he told her with a derisive smile. "Give me your hand."

Childishly, she held her hands behind her back, but Scott dragged her left hand free, and a few moments later the diamond sparkled on her finger.

"Scott, I wouldn't be the right kind of wife for you," she whispered hoarsely, her throat tightening with emotion.

He pressed his lips against the ring and smiled down at her with a certain amount of tolerance in his expression, and her heart behaved in a decidedly odd fashion as he whispered, "You'll be perfect."

"You don't know me very well."

"We'll have the rest of our lives to get to know each other better."

Anna had wanted to avoid his arms for a moment longer, but when he reached for her she melted against him weakly, and his hands moulded her softness against the hard outline of his body. It was virtually impossible to think rationally while his warm lips trailed a destructive path along the sensitive cord of her neck, and a shiver of delight rippled through her.

"Why shouldn't you marry Scott?" the indignant voice of her conscience demanded. "You like him well enough, and physically he doesn't repulse you, so what is there to stop you from accepting what he's offering?"

Nothing stopped her from accepting his offer of marriage, she finally admitted to herself reluctantly.

"Scott . . ." she began unsteadily, but her voice faltered with nervousness.

"Yes, my love?" he prompted without raising his dark head.

She regained her wavering courage somehow and whispered, "I'll marry you."

"I told you you would, didn't I?" he laughed softly against her throat, and his remark sparked off a flame of anger within her which was being doused swiftly by her sense of humour.

"You're an arrogant, insufferable beast!" she accused him, but her voice lacked the angry disapproval she had felt a moment ago.

"Yes, my love," he murmured solemnly, tantalising her with feather-light kisses until she reached up and placed a hand on either side of his face.

"I think I hate you," she said in a voice that sounded unlike her own because of the emotions he had aroused in her, then she dragged his lips down to hers and kissed him with a voluntary passion that seemed to surprise him into immobility for a fraction of a second before he crushed her against him with a fervour that was painful, yet satisfying.

"How long are you going to make me wait before I'll

be able to call you my own?" he demanded eventually, giving her the opportunity to catch her breath and to subdue the pulsating desire he had aroused so expertly.

"A month."

"As long as that?" he thundered, a hint of incredulity in his eyes as she stepped from the circle of his arms and walked across to the window to stare out at the stars glittering in the velvety black sky.

"I must give a month's notice at the Caribbean, and . . . and I would like to be married here at Amazibu Bay, if that's possible," she said without turning, shying away mentally from the idea of being married in Johannesburg with Andrew and Debbie to witness the ceremony.

"You want a big wedding?"

Anna shook her head and, with a peculiar tightness in her throat, she stared down at the ring sparkling on her finger. "I would prefer a quiet wedding, but I would like it to be in a church, and with my father giving me away."

"That sounds reasonable enough," he replied with surprising amiability as he came up behind her and turned her to face him.

"It's a beautiful ring, Scott, and it fits perfectly," she said in nervous haste, shutting her mind to everything except the present as she fought against the ridiculous tears which threatened to choke her. "How did you manage it?"

"An inspired guess," he told her, sliding a lazy finger across her cheek, but she deliberately avoided his fiery glance.

"Shouldn't we go and tell your aunt about our engagement?"

"Aunt Dorrie can wait a little longer," he remonstrated firmly, and several minutes passed before they eventually left the study.

Anna's cheeks were flushed, her eyes almost feverishly bright as she walked beside Scott, and when they finally faced Dorothy MacPherson in the living-room with their news, Anna still felt strangely lightheaded as a result of Scott's recent lovemaking.

"I can't tell you how delighted I am," his aunt exclaimed happily, hugging and kissing them both warmly. "The occasion demands champagne, Scott."

"I have a bottle waiting on ice," he smiled a little mischievously before he disappeared down the passage once more, leaving the two women alone for a few minutes.

"He must have been very sure you would agree to marry him," the older woman smiled, her deep blue eyes twinkling with merriment as she drew Anna down on to the sofa beside her. "I must admit I was very much afraid he wouldn't marry again."

"Afraid?"

"He was very embittered when Trudie died," Mrs. MacPherson told her confidentially, but the sound of approaching footsteps prevented her from saying more.

"Where are the glasses, Aunt Dorrie?" Scott asked, placing the small bucket on the glass table and removing the bottle of champagne from its resting place amongst the ice.

His aunt rose instantly to produce three champagne glasses as if she, too, had been prepared for this very occasion. "Here they are, dear boy."

Inevitably Anna found herself seated beside Scott on the sofa with a glass of champagne in her hand, and she wondered suddenly just what she had let herself in for by agreeing to marry him.

"To us, Anna," he said, touching the rim of his glass to hers before raising it to his lips, and she followed his example, aware of his aunt watching them with an expression of undisguised happiness on her face.

"When is the wedding to be?" his aunt asked eventually, and Anna felt her nerves jar at the mention of the ceremony yet to come which would be so absolutely binding.

"Anna intends making me wait a month," she heard Scott reply in his deep voice, and her pulse quickened as she felt his fingers caress the nape of her neck.

Dorothy MacPherson smiled knowingly. "A month isn't an eternity, you know."

"It feels like an eternity at the moment," Scott grunted, his eyes faintly accusing as they met Anna's.

"Well, I've had my champagne, so I'm going to leave the two of you alone to discuss your plans further," his aunt announced tactfully, placing her glass on the tray and rising to her feet.

"You don't have to go yet, Mrs. MacPherson," Anna protested hastily, afraid suddenly to be alone with Scott, but the older woman merely smiled and shook her head firmly.

"That's kind of you, my dear, but I was young once too, and I know how much the two of you want to be alone."

She could not have been more wrong, Anna thought frantically as Dorothy MacPherson wished them goodnight, and suddenly she was alone with Scott, and shrinking inwardly as an uncomfortable silence settled between them.

"More champagne?" Scott asked after a few nerve-racking seconds as he retrieved the empty glass from between her trembling fingers and placed it beside his own on the tray.

Anna shook her head, his nearness affecting her receptive senses as she murmured, "No, thank you."

He turned towards her, then, and placed his arm along the back of the sofa behind her shoulders. He did not touch her, but his glance slid over her like a slow caress that made her skin tingle and left her feeling peculiarly weak.

"You're so very beautiful," he said at last, his voice vibrantly low and sensually arousing as he added: "I'm finding it extremely difficult to keep my hands off you."

"Scott —" she began, intending to reprimand him, but her throat tightened as her heartbeats quickened erratically in response to his remark.

"I wouldn't be human if I didn't want you," he mocked her, leaning forward to place a hand on the armrest beside her, and imprisoning her in her seat.

"Please ..." she managed chokingly, her desire to escape increasing as she felt the unaccustomed heat surging from her neck into her cheeks.

"I've never seen you blush before," he teased mercilessly, his eyes glittering dangerously as they raked her face. "Does it embarrass you to know that I'm anxious to possess your body?"

Anna felt as though her breath was being squeezed from her lungs at the thought of Scott possessing her physically, and the flush that stained her cheeks seemed to spread systematically throughout her entire body.

"Scott, will you please stop it!" she ordered, but to her dismay her voice sounded shaky and tinged with panic.

His firm mouth curved sensually. "If I stop talking I just might resort to kissing you, so which do you prefer?"

"You're not being fair," she gasped, the clean male smell of him overpowering her senses and making her yearn inexplicably for the kisses he had threatened her with.

"Am I behaving like a beast?"

"A brute," she corrected swiftly.

"An arrogant, insufferable brute of a beast," he laughed softly against her lips, and her valiant efforts to resist him crumbled as she found herself melting helplessly into his embrace.

"You're impossible," she laughed shakily moments before his lips claimed hers in a shattering kiss that left her clinging limply and breathlessly to him with her flushed face buried against the hollow of his broad shoulder.

"You won't change your mind about marrying me, will you?" he demanded softly just above her ear.

"I have a feeling that if I should change my mind you'd never give me a moment's peace."

His arms tightened about her. "I would hound you day and night until you agree to marry me out of sheer desperation."

"I believe you would, but . . ." she hesitated, biting her lip at the flicker of guilt that stirred within her, "I hope you won't regret it."

"I shall never regret wanting you for my wife," he said adamantly, and her hair, flashing a reddish-gold in the light of the table lamp, was spread out across the dark sleeve of his jacket as his mouth found hers with a mastery that set her nerve-ends tingling wildly in response.

Anna was unable to think clearly as she lay in Scott's arms, allowing him to caress her until her emotions soared to unbelievable heights, but later, as she snuggled deeper beneath the sheets in the privacy of her room and stared into the moonlit darkness, she seriously considered what she had done. With the unfamiliarity of Scott's ring on her finger came the realisation that she had agreed to marry him while she still loved Andrew. She could not deny that Scott attracted her physically like a moth to a flame, awakening emotions she was becoming ashamed of, and making her increasingly aware of her own need for fulfilment, but would physical desire be enough to last them through a lifetime of togetherness?

Anna groaned softly into the darkness as she wondered what had possessed her to agree to this marriage. She had no illusions about her own feelings, and neither was she bluffing herself into thinking that Scott harboured an undying love for her. It was for him, as much as for herself, a physical thing. He found her attractive, and possibly considered she would be an asset to his business, but that was all.

Love did not enter into their relationship, and she was somehow grateful for that, for she could never love anyone again the way she had loved Andrew. It had been a love which had almost destroyed her in the process, and she could not prevent herself from laying the blame at Andrew's door. He had known how she felt about him, for she had made no secret of the fact that she had loved him, but as the years slipped by he had made no effort to reciprocate her love, and fear of losing him had almost succeeded in changing her entire personality. Deep inside her there was still that insatiable and uncharitable desire to lash out at Andrew for the pain he had caused her, and Scott, without realising it, had become her weapon against the hurt.

Morris was not at all surprised when she told him of her engagement. He had, so he told Anna, been expecting it for some time. Sheila was naturally a little more reserved with her remarks considering the discussion they had had, but she was happy for Anna's sake nevertheless. Only Anna's parents still had to be told, and she telephoned them from the privacy of her room that Sunday evening. It was not an easy task explaining to her surprised parents that she had agreed to marry a man they had never met or heard of before, but she somehow managed to do so and to sound convincingly happy.

The first hurdle had been traversed and the rest of the month passed with breathtaking swiftness for Anna as, with Sheila's help, she selected a wedding dress and a suitable trousseau for the week she and Scott were to spend at one of his hotels on the north coast after their wedding.

Her parents travelled down to Amazibu Bay by car a week before the time, and Scott made arrangements for them to stay at his home; an arrangement which gave them the opportunity to get to know their future son-in-law. Scott's behaviour, as always, was impeccable, and Charles and Elizabeth Lindsay were not hesitant in making it known that they were pleased with Anna's choice. Andrew and Debbie's names were tactfully not mentioned, but Anna could tell that they were in her parents' thoughts as much as in her own.

Two days before their wedding Anna also moved into Scott's home to be with her parents, and on the afternoon of her arrival there her mother found her pacing the floor of her bedroom like a restless animal. Elizabeth Lindsay was still slender for her age although her reddish-gold hair was flecked with grey, and there was a look of concern in her green eyes as she closed the door softly behind her to observe Anna closely for a moment.

"Anna, my dear," she said at last, approaching her daughter who was almost the image of herself when she was younger, "you're not just marrying Scott on the rebound, are you? You do love him?"

"I'm very fond of him," Anna evaded the question, but

her mother was not satisfied.

"I want to know if you love him," she insisted, her usually soft mouth tightening in a way Anna knew only too well.

"To love someone, Mother, is a painful experience I have no wish to repeat," she said eventually, turning towards the window to stare out across the garden, while at the same time avoiding the intense scrutiny of those eyes which often saw too much. "I'm fond of Scott, and I think we could make a success of our marriage."

"Your father and I like him very much."

"I'm glad," Anna sighed, smiling faintly as she glanced back at her mother with affected casualness. She sensed the reason for her mother's concern, and broached the subject hovering in the air between them. "How are Andrew and Debbie?"

Her mother's expression clouded slightly. "They're well and happy, I suppose."

"What do you mean . . . you suppose?" Anna insisted, a nasty little suspicion taking shape in her mind.

"Well, I don't see them all that often now that they're setting up a home of their own, so I can only presume that they're happy," Elizabeth Lindsay replied defensively. "They send their love, and wish you all the happiness you deserve."

"I'm sure they do," Anna replied cynically, pulling the pins from her hair and brushing the life back into it.

"This isn't like you, Anna," her mother rebuked her gently, and Anna lowered her brush instantly to meet her mother's steady regard in the mirror.

"I'm sorry," she murmured apologetically. "Sometimes the hurt is still there, but I've learnt to live with it lately."

"It will be different once you're married to Scott.

You'll see," her mother replied confidently, but Anna was not so sure that she would ever be free of the pain and the longing she often still experienced. She was going to marry Scott, but Andrew would always be there between them to haunt her.

"Where is everyone?" she asked eventually, dragging herself free of her painful thoughts and changing the subject.

"They're all down on the terrace waiting for us and, if I know your father, he's most probably boring poor Scott to tears with his adventures that time he was at sea," her mother laughed, and then, as they left the room and made their way down to join the others, she said: "This really is a beautiful house, Anna. Will you be making this your home?"

"I suppose so, yes," Anna replied, making an effort to hide her listlessness. "It's so enormous that I'm convinced I shall lose myself in it some day."

"You'll be thankful for the space when you've started a family, my dear," her mother assured her, and Anna stiffened beside her as they stepped out on to the terrace.

Having children had never entered into her plans for the future, but she supposed it was inevitable that she and Scott would eventually have a family. Her colour rose sharply at the prospect of having his children, but she brushed aside this disturbing thought when she saw Scott, imposing and immaculate, and reclining comfortably in a chair while he listened intently to something her father was saying.

At their approach Scott rose politely to his feet and poured them something to drink, indicating with a gesture of one strong, beautifully shaped hand that Anna should take the chair beside his own. She was indescribably tense as she listened to her mother chatting to

Dorothy MacPherson as if they were old friends, but her own powers of conversation failed her for some reason. Scott and her father were discussing the possibility of an oil slick on the beaches as a result of two oil tankers colliding some distance off the coast, but Anna thought only of the way her own life had collided with Scott's.

His hand reached casually and unobtrusively for hers, and she turned her hand palm upwards into his. It was an involuntary action, but the pressure of his fingers made her aware of his strength, and she found his touch oddly comforting at that moment.

Scott's lawyer, Joshua Gray, put in an appearance after dinner that evening, and in the privacy of the study, with Scott and the lawyer observing her closely, Anna read through the marriage contract which had been drawn up according to Scott's instructions. The contents dismayed her considerably, for Scott intended giving her a twenty-five per cent share in his business. It was a magnanimous gesture, but one which she could not accept.

"Could I see you alone for a moment, please, Scott?"

Scott shot a silent request in the lawyer's direction, and Mr. Gray smiled understandingly as he rose and left the room discreetly.

"Is there something in that contract that isn't to your satisfaction, Anna?" Scott wanted to know the moment the door closed behind the gaunt-looking man in the dark suit.

"You're being outrageously generous, Scott," she explained without hesitation, "and I can't accept it."

"Why not?"

"You make me feel as though I'm marrying you for your money."

"Don't be ridiculous!"

His tight-lipped expression conveyed a hidden anger, but she persisted relentlessly. "I mean it, Scott. I can't accept such generosity from you."

"I can afford to be generous."

"I don't doubt that you can afford it, but –"

"You're a business woman at heart, my love, and that's why I've done this," he insisted abruptly, turning towards the door with infuriating self-assurance. "I'll let Joshua in so we can get this business settled."

"*No!*" She flung the contract on to the desk and rose agitatedly to her feet. "I *can't* accept your generosity, Scott. I appreciate it, but I –"

"Anna!" he interrupted sharply, spanning her waist with his hands and drawing her against him. "Marriage is a fifty-fifty business, isn't it?"

"I agree, but –"

"By giving you shares in my business, I'm giving you an interest, and a certain amount of independence. Is that so terrible?"

She could understand his reasoning, but she felt incredibly guilty at the thought of accepting so much from him, and giving so little in return. Although she was certain that his reasons for marrying her were just as selfish as her own, she found it difficult to accept more than she felt was her due.

"Scott . . ."

His lips sealed hers in a lingering kiss that sent a familiar weakness surging into her limbs, and her firmly compressed lips quivered and parted in response beneath the demanding pressure of his.

"I want it this way," he said at length against her mouth, and her hands unconsciously caressed his arms where she could feel the hardness of his muscles beneath the soft material of his light-weight jacket.

"It seems to me you'll always have your way with everything." she murmured in a slightly censorious voice.

"Not everything, my love," he corrected, the intensity of his deep blue eyes disturbing her pulse rate anew. "Just the important things, such as making you my legal marriage and business partner."

Despite her efforts, she could not brush aside her feeling of guilt, and she moved away from the circle of his arms and bit her lip nervously. "I hope you won't regret your decision."

"I'm certain I shan't," he replied adamantly, opening the door to admit the lawyer once more.

The contract was signed and witnessed without further protest from Anna, and little else remained to be done before the actual marriage ceremony was to take place in the local church.

Contrary to what Anna had expected, she was calm and composed on the day she was to be married. Dorothy MacPherson and Anna's mother were the ones who appeared to be jittery about the occasion, and Charles, too, seemed to be fiddling unnecessarily with his tie. It had taken quite a lot of manipulation on their part to keep Scott away from her the previous evening. It was supposedly unlucky for the groom to see the bride on the eve of the wedding, and although Anna secretly laughed at their attempts, she was grateful for the opportunity to be alone with her thoughts. She had to come to terms with herself, and with the future, but with Scott around it would have been impossible to think of anything except his disturbing nearness. Even now, as she sat beside her father in the car that drove them to the church, she could feel her pulse quicken at the prospect of standing beside Scott at the altar. She might not ever love him the way she had loved Andrew, but he had certainly awakened her to emotions she had never suspected she possessed. Perhaps, in time, he would also satisfy the insatiable longing that filled her heart.

Anna looked serenely beautiful in her white wedding dress and veil when she entered the church and walked slowly down the aisle on her father's arm. Scott, who had risen at her entrance, stood awaiting her with an inscrutable expression on his lean face, but a nerve pulsed visibly on the side of his square jaw to indicate that he was not unmoved, and his tall, immaculate presence succeeded in banishing that little flicker of doubt which had reared its head for a fraction of a second.

With only her parents, Scott's aunt, and a few of their close friends present, the ceremony was not a lengthy affair, and before long they emerged from the old stone building with its tall spire as husband and wife. It had all been accomplished with a minimum of fuss, and there was an unreality about it all that lingered until they were driving northwards on their honeymoon. It was at that point that the reality shook Anna to her senses. She was Scott's wife; his to possess, and the plain gold band which had joined the diamond solitaire on her finger was there to prove it.

Fear shivered through her momentarily until Scott, as if sensing her uneasiness, took her hand in his and held it for a few seconds. It was a comforting gesture she had known before, and she smiled, relaxing slightly in the cushioned interior of the car for the first time since their departure from Amazibu Bay.

CHAPTER FIVE

From Scott's private suite in the hotel Anna could look out across the quiet holiday resort which was situated several kilometres north of Durban, and the peaceful tranquillity of the wooded coastline appealed to her after the hectic few days before their wedding. She was, however, unusually tense that evening throughout dinner, and Scott tactfully took a turn around the gardens of the hotel later that evening, giving Anna the opportunity to have the suite to herself for a time.

She bathed and changed into the frothy lace nightgown Sheila had helped her to select for her honeymoon, and she made certain she was in bed when Scott eventually entered the room. He removed his jacket and tie and, flinging them into a chair, he undid the buttons of his shirt, revealing the wide expanse of his tanned, muscular chest as he came towards her.

"You looked exceptionally beautiful today, Mrs. Beresford," he remarked with an enigmatic expression in his deep blue eyes as he stood gazing down at her. "I'm a very fortunate man to have such a lovely wife, and a very desirable one, too, I might add."

For some reason she could not explain, his remark irritated her. "I wish you wouldn't say things like that."

"It's the truth," he insisted. "You're beautiful and desirable ... and you're *mine*."

A faintly mocking smile curved his sensual mouth as he strode towards the bathroom and closed the door firmly behind him. It was too late now to change her mind, she realised with a hollow feeling in her chest, and her tension increased rapidly when she heard him whistling softly to himself while he showered. Could a marriage such as theirs work? Could she spend the rest of her life with Scott while still loving someone else?

Anna closed her eyes for a moment, shutting out her dubious thoughts. She had made her decision, and there was no sense in allowing her mind to be filled with doubts at this moment. Andrew belonged to the past, and she would have to make sure that he remained there.

"Are you tired?"

Her nerves reacted violently to the sound of Scott's voice and her eyes flew open to find him standing beside the bed in a brown silk dressing gown, with his hair dark and glistening with dampness from the shower.

"A little tired, yes," she admitted, a frantic desire for escape gripping her as she glimpsed the unmistakable gleam in his eyes that told her of his desire.

"It's been a long day, and I don't recall having had the opportunity to kiss the bride properly."

"How remiss of you," she replied, adopting a slightly mocking attitude to hide her nervousness, but her heart hammered wildly as he lowered himself on to the bed and imprisoned her by placing a hand on either side of her body.

"It's a slight error which I intend to rectify at once," he told her smoothly, and lowering his head he proceeded to do just that.

After a few frightening seconds she began to respond to his kisses, but, when his conquering lips strayed along the column of her throat and across her shoulder to brush aside the flimsy strap of her nightgown, she knew again a moment of panic.

"Scott . . ."

His mouth sought the enchanting curve of her breast.

"Yes, my love?"

"It ... doesn't matter," she whispered unsteadily, intoxicated now by the fiery touch of his lips and hands on her trembling, responsive body.

As if sensing an inherent shyness in her, he flung out an arm and switched off the light. There was a faint rustle as he removed his dressing gown, and the next moment he had thrust aside the sheets and was lying beside her, the warmth of his hard body against her own awakening her to a multitude of sensations she had never known. She felt him tremble against her, but, curbing his impatience, he continued to arouse her in an unhurried manner until fear and thoughts of withdrawal no longer existed beyond the sweet ecstasy of her need as it rose sharply to match his.

She went to sleep in Scott's arms that night, with her head resting comfortably on his shoulder. There had been no need for her to be afraid, she realised moments before she fell asleep. Scott had proved to be a very gentle and considerate lover, and she would always be eternally grateful to him for that.

The honeymoon which she had secretly dreaded turned out to be a time she would always remember with a certain tenderness and joy. They spent the week going for long walks, soaking up the sun on the sandy beach, or driving out into the surrounding countryside to linger in the picturesque valleys of the sugar cane country. It was a time, too, of getting to know each other, and Anna discovered that her husband's mocking, sometimes cynical attitude hid a sensitive nature that made him infinitely more human and approachable, and it was with something close to regret that she eventually packed their suitcases for their return journey to Amazibu Bay.

Dorothy MacPherson was there to welcome them back,

and Scott carried their suitcases up to the master bedroom which had been redecorated in colours ranging from white to deep lilac. Anna would have felt decidedly uncomfortable in that room had she not learnt a few weeks before their marriage that Scott's first wife had preferred the suite on the west side of the house. The master bedroom had not been occupied since the death of Scott's parents, and Anna had been strangely relieved to discover this.

"Are you sorry the honeymoon is over?" Scott asked, coming up behind her while she unpacked their suitcases and, placing his hands possessively over the flat of her stomach, he explored the sensitive cord of her neck with his lips.

"Yes and no," she sighed, leaning back against the hardness of his body and savouring the delight of his touch. "It was wonderful while it lasted, but we had to get back to reality some time."

"It seems as though I've acquired a very sensible wife," he teased, turning her to face him and drawing her wholly into his arms.

She relaxed in his embrace, thrilling to the caress of his lips and hands until she was forced to hold him off with her palms spread out against his chest.

"I'm not being very sensible at the moment," she whispered tremulously, her heart quickening at the storm of passion in his glance. "The suitcases must be unpacked, and your aunt is expecting us to join her for tea," she added weakly, warding off his lips.

"The suitcases and the tea can wait," he muttered thickly, lifting her effortlessly and carrying her towards the large bed, where Cupid, carved into the ornamental headboard, smiled benignly down at them.

When Anna was finally able to continue with the task

of unpacking, there was an unmistakable glow about her of which she was quite oblivious. Scott, after a quick shower and a change of clothing, hesitated in the bedroom door before going down to join his aunt, and his teasing glance lingered briefly on her slender curves which were unsuccessfully hidden beneath the loose folds of the silk dressing gown she had wrapped about her.

"It's just as well no one can see you now."

"Why not?" she asked innocently, unaware of the tender smile curving her full, sensitive mouth as she allowed her glance to slide down the length of his lean, immaculate frame.

"A discerning eye will notice the signs of a woman who's been made love to recently."

His remark stained her cheeks a delicate pink, but she held his glance unwaveringly as she approached him. "Would it matter if I'm that obvious?"

"Not to me, it wouldn't," he mocked her, sliding his hands across the rounded curve of her hips and drawing her hard against him. "A cool, untouched appearance draws more attention and speculation than the glowing look on the face of a woman who's been married only a week."

"You're trying to embarrass me," she accused him with a reproving glance.

"Only because it's still such a novelty to see you blush like a schoolgirl," he explained in his usual unperturbed manner, kissing her quickly before he released her and strode from the room.

The honeymon was over in more ways than one, and Anna found herself acting as Scott's part-time secretary, as well as taking over the household responsibilities from his aunt, who was only too grateful to relinquish some of her duties.

"My legs just can't take it any more," she complained one morning, sinking into a chair on the terrace while Anna poured their tea. "I can't tell you what a relief it is to be able to depend on your help, Anna. Trudie never once ..." She hesitated, casting a guilty glance over her shoulder as Anna placed her tea on the small table beside her chair. "I suppose I shouldn't be telling you this, but you might as well know that Trudie's only interest was in spending money as fast as she could lay her hands on it, and that's where the trouble started."

"What trouble?" Anna asked curiously, the desire to know more about Scott's first wife like an irritating thorn which had to be removed.

Making sure that they were alone, Dorothy MacPherson drew her chair closer to Anna's. "The marriage was a mistake from the start. Scott realised this very soon after their marriage, I'm sure, but he isn't the kind of man to shirk his responsibilities, and he was determined to make the best of it. Trudie thrived on a wild social life, but Amazibu Bay hadn't much to offer in that respect, and she soon became bored and dissatisfied. Scott tried to encourage her to take an interest in other things, but Trudie scorned his suggestions and there were plenty of arguments. She finally ran off with George Warren, a man she had met at the home of friends, and soon afterwards they died in a car crash not far from here." Aunt Dorrie sipped at her tea before adding firmly, "She would have ruined Scott eventually, mentally and financially, if she'd had the opportunity."

Anna felt a flicker of compassion for Scott, but she saw something of her sister in the bored, dissatisfied Trudie which did not exactly please her, and she mentally brushed aside the distasteful subject.

Less than a week later Anna and Scott received an

unexpected visit from Dennis and Joan Mulder. Dennis managed one of Scott's hotels in Johannesburg, and from Scott's shuttered expression she gathered that he was not at all thrilled at the thought of entertaining their guests, but, despite this, he seemed to get along on a fairly friendly basis with Dennis Mulder.

Anna liked Dennis instantly. Fair, and slightly on the stout side, with grey eyes that were lively and warm, he made her feel at ease instantly. But his wife, Joan, sat rigidly in her chair, maintaining a stony silence despite Anna's efforts to engage her in conversation.

Auburn-haired, dark-eyed, and sophisticated, Joan somehow managed to convey her disapproval, but it was some time before Anna gathered that her disapproval was being directed at Scott. This surprised and puzzled Anna, but it was not until the two men excused themselves to look up certain information in Scott's study that Joan Mulder came alive for the first time, and Anna began to discover the reason for this woman's strange behaviour.

"Trudie, Scott's first wife, and I were very close friends," she announced in her husky voice, her dark eyes appraising Anna thoughtfully.

"Really?"

The dark eyes hardened, and the thin lips tightened. "It was Scott's fault, of course, that their marriage didn't succeed."

"Was it?"

"His jealousy and possessiveness drove her into the arms of another man."

Anna felt herself go stiff with resentment. "It's not a crime to be possessive, and jealousy is something which can be invoked."

"That may be so, but both ingredients can destroy a marriage," Joan insisted, her hand clenching the glass so tightly that Anna expected it to splinter into fragments at any moment. "Scott's only concern was for his business, and he never cared one jot for Trudie's happiness."

"There are two sides to every story, Mrs. ... er ... Joan," Anna corrected herself hastily, staring down into the amber liquid in her own glass. "Perhaps they were just incompatible."

"There was much more to it than that," Joan persisted harshly, her cynical glance sweeping Anna's elegant figure in the beige-coloured silk creation which Scott had bought for her while they were on honeymoon. "I bet Scott hasn't wasted time in making sure you take an interest in the hotel business."

Joan was being deliberately offensive, and Anna bit back the angry words that sprang to her lips, but her voice sounded clipped with the effort. "Scott hasn't actually insisted on my doing anything in particular. If I have become involved in his business affairs, then I've done so quite freely, and mainly because I enjoy it."

"Take care that you don't bite off more than you can chew, as they say," Joan snapped sarcastically.

Anna observed her for a moment in silence, contemplating the desire to put this woman in her place, but deciding against it mainly for Scott's sake. "Surely you occasionally help your husband in some way?" Anna's eyebrows rose fractionally, and a flicker of distaste was mirrored in her eyes as she said : "You must find life extremely boring."

"Not at all," the rigid-faced woman remarked, swallowing down the remainder of her drink and placing the delicately cut glass on the table beside her chair. "Dennis and I go out as often as we can. He plays bowls, and I play tennis, and we're both very fond of making up a foursome for an evening of bridge." She glanced speculatively at Anna. "Do you play bridge?"

"I'm afraid I don't."

For the first time that evening Anna saw Joan's thin lips twist into a semblance of a smile. "Trudie was an excellent bridge player, and so was George."

"How nice," Anna said coldly, realising intuitively that Joan Mulder must have had a hand in encouraging the friendship between Scott's wife and her boy-friend.

"I could never imagine what Trudie saw in Scott. He's arrogant and overbearing, and really rather dull despite his attractiveness."

Anna stared at Joan for a moment, wondering whether she had heard correctly, but then she found herself fighting back the laughter that bubbled up in her throat. It was obvious that something else lurked behind Joan Mulder's unexpected statement. Scott could be overbearing, forceful, and arrogant at times, but dull? *Never!*

"I can't say I've found him dull at any time," she managed eventually, thinking of Scott's vitality, and his masculine virility which had stirred her senses from the moment they had met until she had finally been overpowered by it.

The suggestion of a sneer touched Joan's thin lips. "The trouble with you is, you're still too much in love with him to notice his faults."

Too much in love with him! The words swirled through Anna's mind, and she could not help wondering what Joan Mulder would say if she should disclose the fact that she had married Scott while still loving someone else. The thought brought a smile to her unwilling lips, and she said quietly:

"Perhaps you're right."

Their conversation ended as the men returned to the

living-room, and Anna looked at Dennis a little more closely. Drawing comparisons was unfair and unkind, but, beside Scott, Dennis was rather plain and ordinary, and although she liked Dennis very much, she could not prevent herself from wondering whether there had not been a certain amount of envy attached to Joan's remarks with regard to Scott.

"What did the Mulders want last night?" Scott's aunt wanted to know when Anna joined her for tea on the terrace the following morning.

"I think they came mainly out of curiosity," Anna said tritely as she helped herself to a biscuit, then she smiled mischievously at the older woman. "I noticed you made yourself scarce the moment they arrived."

Dorothy MacPherson made a disparaging gesture which was quite unlike her. "I never could stand that woman, and I think the feeling is mutual."

Anna's expression sobered. "I don't think she likes me very much, either, for marrying the man who was once her friend's husband."

"Don't let that worry you, my dear, but keep away from that woman," Aunt Dorrie warned. "She's poison."

Anna allowed her glance to wander over the sun-drenched garden as she recalled her conversation with Joan Mulder the previous evening, and a frown creased her usually smooth brow.

"Tell me, Aunt Dorrie," she began thoughtfully, "what exactly has Joan Mulder got against Scott?"

"What do you mean?"

"Well, her animosity towards him was so evident that it was almost tangible," Anna explained. "Is it because of Trudie? Or is there perhaps another reason?"

Dorothy MacPherson looked away. "I wouldn't know."

"You might as well tell me, Aunt Dorrie," Anna insisted, sensing a certain wariness in the older woman to
discuss the subject. "I'll find out sooner or later, but I
would rather hear it from you."

Aunt Dorrie hesitated, poured herself a second cup of
tea, and stirred it with unnecessary vigour. "I know I
shouldn't be telling you this, and Scott will never forgive
me, but ..." She glanced guiltily over her shoulder, but
with Scott away on business for the day, and with the
servants out of sight, she continued in a lowered voice.
"Joan Mulder was silly enough to make a pass at Scott
once, before he was married. He was interested, but he
gave her the brush-off when he met Trudie. I don't think
she'll ever forgive him entirely for that."

"Oh," Anna breathed faintly, making an effort to
swallow down her laughter, but it proved to be too much
for her and it was several seconds before she managed to
control herself sufficiently to speak. "Oh, dear, I shouldn't
be laughing about something so serious, because it's
really quite pathetic, but ..." She dabbed at her eyes
with an ineffectual lace handkerchief and met the older
woman's amused glance. "I knew there had to be something, but I never imagined it would be because Scott
had rebuffed her attentions."

"Men usually prefer to do the chasing, but if you ask
me, Joan Mulder is quite capable of having her little affairs without her husband's knowledge, and she's just as
capable of spreading plenty of venom," Aunt Dorrie
remarked seriously. "I know for a fact that she encouraged Trudie's relationship with that George Warren."

"Tell me about Trudie. What was she like?"

"She was jealous and possessive in the extreme before
George Warren arrived on the scene," Aunt Dorrie declared distastefully, contradicting Joan Mulder's state-

ment completely about Scott having been a jealous, possessive husband. "Scott dared not even look at another woman, or they'd end up having the most awful rows," his aunt continued. "Scott is the kind of man who attracts women, and I don't deny that he has a certain charm which even I find irresistible at times, but he was never unfaithful to Trudie while he was married to her."

A question hovered on Anna's lips, and it all at once became imperative that she should know the answer. "Were there many women in his life during the past two years after Trudie's death?"

"There were several, but Scott was determined never to marry again, and apparently decided that there was safety in numbers, so to speak," his aunt smiled with a hint of mischief in her deep blue eyes. "He changed his mind very quickly, though, after meeting you, Anna, and you've made him happy during the few short weeks you've been married. You *must* know that."

"Scott is a very difficult person to get to know," Anna replied thoughtfully. "I don't think anyone will ever get close enough to him to know exactly what he's thinking, or what he really feels."

Aunt Dorrie did not contradict this as she glanced speculatively at Anna. "Has he spoken much of his previous marriage to you?"

"He mentioned it once, and then only briefly."

"And you haven't questioned him about it," Aunt Dorrie stated knowingly.

"No." Anna gestured dismissively with her hands. "It's really something that's over and done with as far as I'm concerned, but some of the things Joan Mulder said last night made me curious to know more."

"What did she say?"

"Oh, nothing of importance," Anna smiled reassuringly. "She was mostly bent on tearing Scott apart, and impressing me with the fact that she and Trudie were such close friends."

During the ensuing silence a mynah bird screeched noisily in the flamboyant tree, causing a stir amongst the smaller birds, and succeeding in making them seek refuge elsewhere from the scorching sun.

"Whatever Joan Mulder may have told you, Anna, don't take it too seriously," Aunt Dorrie interrupted the silence between them. "Scott has worked hard and played hard in the past. He has his faults, just as we all do, but he has certain ideals and principles, and he sticks to them rigidly."

Anna assured her that she had no intention of allowing Joan Mulder's remarks to disturb her in any way.

Scott's business activities took him away from home quite often, but Anna did not object. There was plenty to do and, when she was not pottering about in the garden alongside his aunt during her free time, she enjoyed being alone with her thoughts.

The past was no longer so painful, she discovered to her surprise. She could think of Andrew without flinching, and could almost forgive her sister for taking from her the man she had loved.

The man she had loved!

Anna drew a startled breath. Was that what marriage to Scott has done for her? Had it enabled her to shift her love for Andrew Tait into the past? Would it always remain there, though, she wondered with a touch of cynicism, and how would she feel when she was forced to meet Andrew again at some future date? Would she still be able to keep her love for him in the past where it belonged?

Anna shook herself mentally and went for a leisurely

stroll along the beach. Scott was not expected home until late that evening, and with dinner still an hour away there was no reason for her to stay at home, she decided as she removed the scarf from her hair and felt the cool breeze lifting it playfully off her shoulders.

Without intending to, she walked as far as the bench where Scott had first discussed marriage with her.

"You're going to be mine, Anna. And soon," she vividly recalled him saying as she sat and stared out across the restless sea.

She had initially rejected the idea of marriage to Scott, but under the impact of the emotional influence he had over her she had succumbed, and so far their marriage had not been a failure, although Anna could not help knowing that something vital was missing. Scott had never once said that he loved her, and as for herself? ... she had no love to offer him! She was strongly attracted to him, yes, and she hated him at times when he mocked her so ruthlessly about the passionate response he was able to arouse in her, but love ... ? No! She had loved once, and would never love again!

She sighed irritably and rose to her feet, intending to walk further along the beach, but something caught her eye, and she turned to glance over her shoulder. Scott was walking across the sand towards her with a towel flung carelessly across one broad shoulder, and wearing a pair of blue bathing trunks that hugged his slim hips and accentuated the muscular strength of his long legs.

Anna's knees seemed to weaken beneath her at the sight of that deeply tanned, virile body, and her pulse rate quickened in a now familiar way when he dropped his towel on to the sand and stood observing her with his hands resting characteristically on his hips. His disconcerting blue eyes took in the smoothness of her sun-kissed shoulders beneath the flimsy straps of her summer frock, and lingered for a breathtaking moment where the bodice dipped a little daringly to reveal the shadowy cleft between her breasts.

"You become more beautiful each time I look at you," he said, his cool hands against her warm shoulders moving in a faintly caressing way.

She trembled inwardly at his familiar touch, but she forced herself to remain outwardly cool as she stared up at him. "Flattery has never impressed me."

"Perhaps *this* will," he said abruptly, and she was powerless to resist as he swept her up against him in an embrace that drove the breath from her body. The passionate warmth of his mouth against her own made her realise, not for the first time, how little control she had over her emotions when he was intent upon arousing her.

"Scott, please ..." she begged breathlessly, struggling for release. "Not here on the beach where everyone can see us."

His arms fell away from her, but his eyes held her captive. "These past two days away from you have felt like two years."

"We were only expecting you later this evening," she said half accusingly as she made an effort to recover her shattered composure.

"I managed to get away a little sooner." Cynicism curved his lips. "Are you disappointed?"

"I just didn't expect you, that's all," she prevaricated.

"Did you miss me?"

She stared up at him coldly. "Of *course* I missed you. Life was definitely more peaceful without you hanging about."

The danger signals flashing in his eyes should have warned her, but she was quite unprepared for what happened next. With one swift, flowing movement, he stooped, clamped an arm about her knees, and lifted her unceremoniously across his shoulder as if she were a sack of potatoes.

"So it was peaceful without me, was it?" he demanded harshly, striding out towards the sea.

Anna was too shocked and bewildered to react at once, but as a gnawing suspicion took shape in her mind, she thumped his broad back in helpless frustration.

"Scott!" she screamed hoarsely. "What do you think you're doing?"

"I'm going to dump you in the sea."

"No! No, don't!" she pleaded frantically, but he was deaf to her pleas as he waded into the shallow water and strode purposefully deeper into the sea to where the waves broke about them with a deafening roar. "You'll ruin my dress. Scott! Please!"

The cold sea water struck her body with a chilling force that made her gasp for breath a mere fraction of a second before she became submerged in the swirling mass of salty water. Scott's arm was now clamped firmly about her waist, and she was just beginning to think he would never surface when she was suddenly lifted above the water.

She clung to him weakly as she dragged the air painfully into her lungs and, not knowing whether to laugh or cry, she resorted instead to anger. "You idiot! You imbecile! Look what you've done!"

"Perhaps another dash of the same medicine will cool off your temper," he laughed, and she was plunged into the water a second time before she was lifted free and kissed until it felt as though her very soul was being drawn through her parted lips. "Feeling better, you little firebrand?"

If you were in their place what would you do?

Jeanette...

Though she has survived a heart-wrenching tragedy, is there more unhappiness in store for Jeanette? She is hopelessly in love with a man who is inaccessible to her. Her story will come alive in the pages of "Beyond the Sweet Waters" by Anne Hampson.

Juliet...

Rather than let her father choose her husband, she ran...ran into the life of the haughty duke and his intriguing household on a Caribbean island. It's an intimate story that will stir you as you read "The Arrogant Duke" by Anne Mather.

Laurel...

There was no turning back for Laurel. She was playing out a charade with the arrogant plantation owner, and the stakes were "love". It's all part of a thrilling romantic adventure called "Teachers Must Learn" by Nerina Hilliard.

Fern...

She tried to escape to a new life...a new world...now she was faced with a loveless marriage of convenience. How long could she wait for the love she so strongly craved to come to her... Live with Fern... love with Fern...in the exciting "Cap Flamingo" by Violet Winspear.

Jeanette, Juliet, Laurel, Fern...these are some of the memorable people who come alive in the pages of Harlequin Romance novels. And now, without leaving your home, you can share their most intimate moments!

It's the easiest and most convenient way to get every one of the exciting Harlequin Romance novels! And now with a home subscription plan you won't miss *any* of these true-to-life stories, and you don't even have to go out looking for them.

Get your
Harlequin Romance
Home Subscription NOW!
- Never miss a title!
- Get them first—straight from the presses!
- No additional costs for home delivery!
- These first 4 novels are yours FREE!

Ignoring his remark, she struggled free of his arms and pushed her hair out of her eyes. Laughter fought with anger as she faced him. "You've made me look a mess!"

"You look beautiful even with your hair all stringy and wet, and your dress . . . hm . . ." His mouth curved sensuously as his warm glance lingered on the silky material which clung to her body, revealing every curve for his keen perusal. "You might as well stay in the water now instead of rushing back to change."

Anna's cheeks were flushed as she glanced down at herself ruefully and, to her amazement, she heard herself agreeing to his suggestion. The situation was all at once hilarious, and it no longer mattered whether the beach was deserted or not. If people thought her mad to be swimming about fully clothed, then they were perfectly free to do so.

"What on earth happened to you, Anna?" Dorothy MacPherson demanded, taking in Anna's bedraggled appearance when she arrived at the house with Scott a half hour later.

"I sort of . . . fell into the sea," she explained lamely, flashing an angry glance at Scott who was shaking with inward laughter.

"Hm . . ." Aunt Dorrie grunted, taking in the situation at a glance and making a shrewd guess. "It's more likely you were pushed in, I would say."

"Delay dinner another half hour, Aunt Dorrie, if you can," Scott said laughingly as he drew Anna towards the stairs. "It shouldn't take longer than that for Anna to make herself look a little less like a drowned rat."

"It's *your* fault if I look like a drowned rat," Anna accused him when they reached the privacy of their room. "If you hadn't thrown me into the sea —"

She was silenced effectively by his lips, while at the same time she was made intensely aware of the hardness of his thighs against her own, and the broadness of his chest against her breasts as his hands curved her body into his. His mouth moved urgently against hers, sapping her strength as she struggled against him, and subduing her into trembling acquiescence. She offered no resistance as he divested her of her damp clothing, and her emotions clamoured for an outlet when she felt the heat of his body against her own. One hand slid from her hip to cup the rounded softness of her breast, and she moaned softly against his mouth as intoxicating flames of desire leapt through her veins.

The moment was shattered, however, when Scott raised his head and said with infuriating calmness, "I shall be away again for a few days as from tomorrow."

Surfacing from the depths of her emotions was a painfully slow process, and confused and bewildered by his ability to keep such a rigid control over his emotions, she murmured unsteadily, "Not again, surely?"

"So you missed me after all," he mocked her cruelly, and she broke free of his arms, pulling on a towelling robe as she put some distance between them.

"Where are you going this time?" she asked, unable to look at him while she struggled to regain her composure.

"South. Down to Port Shepstone."

"Do you realise you've been away more often than you've been at home lately?"

"I'm sorry, Anna," he said with a hint of an apology in his deep voice as he came up behind her and turned her relentlessly to face him. "It's just one of the liabilities of my job."

He looked strangely boyish with his dark hair falling

across his broad forehead and, to her dismay, she heard herself asking, "Take me with you, Scott."

"I would prefer you to remain here with Aunt Dorrie."

"Why?" she demanded, swallowing down her disappointment. "Why can't I go with you?"

"Business and pleasure don't mix, my love. And you're a very distracting commodity," he mocked her, twisting a strand of her hair about his fingers as he added: "Even when your hair is hanging about your face like rat's tails you still have that disturbing quality about you."

"You're a beast!" she accused him, jerking her head free and making a dash for the bathroom.

She had no idea what had possessed her to want to go with him on this trip, but she certainly would not thrust her unwanted presence on him if he did not want her, she decided a little churlishly.

Scott left after breakfast the following morning, and two days later a telegram arrived from her mother. Her father was in hospital after suffering a slight thrombosis, the telegram stated, and would she please come to Johannesburg at once. With Scott not expected back for a day or so, and not knowing where exactly to contact him, Anna made the necessary arrangements for a flight to Johannesburg, and bundled a few things into a suitcase.

"I'm sorry about leaving you alone like this, Aunt Dorrie," Anna apologised when she said goodbye to Scott's aunt at the airport.

"I understand, my dear," the older woman replied, kissing Anna's cheek. "Your family need you at this moment, and you must go. I'll explain to Scott when he returns."

Anna nodded silently and a few minutes later she was walking through the gates towards the Boeing waiting out on the tarmac. It was too late now to have any qualms about her decision to go home to her mother, but there was little else she could do under the circumstances. To have had Scott's support would have meant a lot, but she would and *would* manage without him, she told herself firmly.

CHAPTER SIX

The flight to Johannesburg took a little more than an hour, but that was long enough for Anna to realise that her father's sudden illness had precipitated a meeting with Andrew and Debbie. Anna dreaded the thought, but the inevitable could not be avoided, and she hoped fervently that she would have the strength to cope with the situation.

She collected her suitcase once the plane had landed at Jan Smuts, and took a taxi out to Sandton. The long drive gave her the opportunity to steady her quaking nerves, but her attempts to shake off her wariness had been unsuccessful, she discovered when she finally stepped out of the taxi in front of her parents' home and paid off the driver.

Nothing had changed, she realised with something of a shock as she stood at the gate and stared up at the Tudor-style house. Everything still looked the same. The ivy creeper against the house still threatened to obscure the living-room window, and the pergola on the west side of the building was still drooping beneath the weight of the wild-ranking wisteria.

A faint smile quivered on Anna's lips as she hesitated just inside the gate, but it disappeared swiftly as her wary glance swept the length of the empty driveway, then, picking up her suitcase, she walked quickly up the flagstoned path.

Her mother was pale but seemingly composed when she answered the door, but there was something in the manner in which she embraced Anna that hinted at the anxiety she was suffering.

"Anna, my dear! I'm so glad you could come," she said unsteadily, drawing Anna inside and glancing beyond her. "But where's Scott?"

Anna closed the door and, leaving her suitcase in the hall, she led her mother into the living-room as she explained, "Scott wasn't at home this morning when your telegram arrived, so I booked a flight on the first available plane and came on ahead without him. But tell me first ..." she changed the subject to more important matters as she drew her mother down on to the sofa beside her, "How is Daddy?"

"As well as can be expected," Elizabeth Lindsay grimaced as she spoke, her hands moving agitatedly in her lap. "That's the only information I'm able to get out of them at the hospital, but the doctor seemed a little more optimistic this afternoon after receiving the results of the electro-cardiograph."

"Is Daddy conscious?"

"Yes, thank goodness, but he seems to have been connected up to a hundred and one machines that look absolutely frightening." Her eyes grew moist as she gripped Anna's hand tightly. "It's good to have you here with me, dear. You may have inherited my looks, but you're sensible like your father when there's a crisis in the family."

"You haven't been alone all day, have you?" Anna asked carefully, ignoring her mother's remark.

"Debbie spent the morning with me, but Andrew

fetched her again just after lunch," her mother told her. "Anna ... what are we going to do?"

"We're going to have dinner first," Anna replied at once, deliberately misunderstanding her mother. "I haven't had anything to eat since this morning, and I'm famished!"

"Heavens, yes," her mother rose instantly. "Dinner has been ready for ages, but I've been expecting Debbie and Andrew, and ..." The sound of a car coming up the drive made her pause, and Anna felt her stomach nerves grow taut. "That must be them now," her mother added, her questioning glance resting on Anna who had risen nervously to her feet. "Will you let them in, my dear, or shall I?"

There was no sense in delaying the inevitable, Anna decided as she took a firm grip on herself, but she felt decidedly shaky inside as she nodded, and said: "I'll let them in, Mother."

Steeling herself for this meeting with the man who had caused her so much unhappiness once, she walked into the hall and flung open the door just as the doorbell chimed. Debbie stood there, fair and lovely with her elfin-shaped face registering shocked surprise.

"Anna!" she exclaimed, her smile a little hesitant as she stepped inside. "When did you arrive?"

"Just a few minutes ago," Anna replied, and then, realising that Debbie must be as nervous and tense as she was about this meeting, she banished the remnants of her antagonism towards her young sister, and kissed her lightly on the cheek. "You're looking well, Debbie."

"So are you, Anna," her sister smiled, and there was recognisable relief in her grey eyes as she faced Anna. "Where's Mother?"

"In the living-room," Anna told her and, as Debbie

turned away, Anna saw Andrew coming up the steps towards her. Her heart thudded uncomfortably in her
breast when his eyes met hers, and then, for some unaccountable reason, nothing else happened. She steeled
herself automatically against the pain she had known for
so many months, but made instead the startling discovery
that she could look at his tall, lean frame with nothing
more than a flicker of interest. Confused and bewildered
by her reaction to the man she had once loved so desperately, she forced herself to remain calm until she would
have time to analyse the situation level-headedly, and her
voice sounded remarkably casual as she said: "Hello
Andrew."

"Anna ..." His warm glance took in her slender ele-
gance in the pale green summer suit and matching silk
blouse which she had selected for the journey, but his
smile, when it came, no longer had the same devastating
effect on her. "It's good to see you again."

He remained standing on the doorstep, looking at her
in the most peculiar way, until she said abruptly, "Are
you coming in, or do you intend to spend the evening on
the doorstep?"

Andrew stepped inside then, but he lingered beside her
as she closed the door. "You're even more beautiful than
I remembered, Anna."

She stared at him for a moment, taking in the sandy-
coloured hair which still insisted in lying untidily across
his forehead, and the warm brown eyes which had once
had the power to make her heart behave in the most
peculiar way, but at that moment she felt strangely detached as she said: "Thank you" a little coolly, and
brushed past him on her way to the living-room where
her mother and Debbie awaited them.

The conversation did not exactly flow at the dinner

table that evening with everyone's thoughts centred on
Charles Lindsay, but there was also an unaccountable
tension in the atmosphere which puzzled Anna as she became aware of Andrew observing her unobtrusively from
time to time, and she was faintly irritated by his behaviour.

'What's happened to me?' she asked herself silently
when she eventually sat beside her mother in the back of
Andrew's car on the way to the hospital. 'Has reaction
set in, in some peculiar way, to deaden my feelings? Or
is there some other inexplicable reason for this lack of
interest?'

There was no time to ponder over it, however, for they
had arrived at the hospital, and a few minutes later they
filed silently into her father's private ward. The nursing
sister frowned at them and muttered something about her
father not being allowed so many visitors all at once, but
Anna assured her that they would not remain long
enough to tire him.

It was a shock for Anna to see her father, always so
active and healthy, lying there looking so pale and tired
against the pillows, but he smiled his pleasure at seeing
them all together and, with Elizabeth's hand clasping his,
he told them the gratifying news that the doctor was certain he would recover swiftly enough to return home
within two weeks.

The Sister put in an appearance again a few minutes
later and practically ordered them out, but Charles
caught hold of Anna's hand and gestured that she should
remain a moment longer.

"We'll wait outside in the passage for you, my dear,"
her mother said when Anna glanced at her questioningly
and, kissing her husband lightly on the forehead, she
followed Debbie and Andrew from the room.

"Anna..."

"Don't tire yourself, Daddy," she said hastily under the disapproving glance of the uniformed Sister.

"See that your mother doesn't worry too much," he begged softly. "Can I depend on you?"

"You know you can," she smiled, stroking his grey head lightly.

"Your mother gets into a state of panic over the least little thing," he said urgently, gesturing the Sister to silence when she was about to voice her protests again. "I'm going to be all right, so don't let her brood too much."

"I'll see to it that she doesn't."

Charles smiled briefly. "You're a good, sensible girl."

"You must rest now," Anna said hastily, catching the Sister's eye. "We'll come again tomorrow."

He nodded and Anna leaned forward to kiss him on the cheek before she left the ward hurriedly. She found her mother alone in the passage and when she noticed Elizabth's worried expression, she silently cursed Debbie and Andrew for thoughtlessly leaving her alone.

"What did your father want to talk to you about?" she demanded the instant Anna reached her side.

"Daddy was a little anxious about you, Mother, but I managed to assure him that you were perfectly all right."

"Oh." The green eyes filled with tears of relief. "I thought for a moment that he might have told you something he didn't want me to know."

"Don't be silly, Mother," Anna said gently, but firmly as she linked her arm through Elizabeth's and guided her towards the lift. "There's nothing to worry about. Really there isn't."

"Yes," her mother whispered, pulling herself together and managing a shaky smile. "Yes, of course. He's going to be all right. The doctor said so, didn't he?"

Under Anna's steadying influence Elizabeth seemed to shake off her fears by the time they met up with Debbie and Andrew in the parking area, and she spoke tentatively of her plans to take Charles on a lengthy holiday once he was fit to travel again.

Debbie and Andrew had tea with them at the house before returning to their apartment in the city. Debbie seemed to be in a frantic hurry to get away, Anna noticed absently, and Andrew finally said goodnight and followed her from the house with obvious reluctance.

"I'm worried about those two," Elizabeth confessed when they heard Andrew's car speeding down the drive.

"Why should you be worried about them?" Anna asked cautiously as she helped herself to a second cup of tea.

"I don't know," her mother gestured helplessly. "I have this terrible feeling that all is not well with their marriage. I know Debbie too well not to have noticed the signs. She's become quite withdrawn lately, and something is definitely worrying her." Her glance sharpened as it met Anna's. "You must have noticed the change in Andrew as well?"

Anna could have mentioned that he appeared to be more subdued since his marriage to Debbie, but she was not about to place any significance on her casual observations. "Don't allow your imagination to run away with you, Mother. They're most probably going through a sticky patch as all marriages do at some time or another."

"I hope you're right, Anna," her mother sighed heavily.

"I know I am," Anna reassured her, keeping her own doubts to herself.

"Anna ... I didn't want to mention this, but ..." her

mother hesitated, and Anna felt herself stiffen as she guessed what was to follow. "You *have* got over Andrew, haven't you?"

For a moment Anna struggled with her inability to discuss her problems and feelings with anyone, but the need to talk to someone at that moment was overpowering. She needed to thrash out her confusing thoughts in order to understand what had happened to her, and meeting her mother's curious but faintly sympathetic glance, she capitulated.

"I loved him very much, Mother," she admitted setting aside her cup and rising to her feet to pace about as if walking helped her to think clearly. "I spent months trying to get him out of my system, I married Scott while still of the absolute conviction that I would always love Andrew, and then I came face to face with him this evening, and ..." She broke off abruptly and gestured despairingly with her hands. "After the initial shock of seeing him again had passed ... there was nothing! It was like an anti-climax!"

Elizabeth Lindsay leaned forward in her chair and observed her daughter closely. "You mean you don't love him any more?"

"Mother, I'm beginning to wonder whether I *ever* loved him," Anna sighed exasperatedly, and clutching the mantelshelf firmly until her fingers ached, she stared down into the empty grate almost as if she were watching a playback of that evening's events. "I found myself looking at Andrew this evening and wondering just exactly what it was about him that had attracted me so much. It's like watching an old movie and finding that the interesting bits are now not so interesting after all. It's confusing, and quite frightening, to discover that a love as strong as the love I thought I had for Andrew could just disintegrate into nothing."

"Have you ever thought of the possibility that you might never have loved him at all? That you were merely in love with love, as they say?" her mother suggested gently.

Anna frowned down at the woman seated so calmly in the padded armchair close to her. "Do you mean to say that I wasted all those years of my life loving a man because I was merely in love with the idea of love?"

"It's a possibility you can't overlook."

"It's a possibility I don't even want to think about," Anna replied tritely, discarding the idea almost angrily, but it lingered hauntingly in her subconscious.

"And Scott?" her mother broke the turbulent silence. "What about Scott?"

"How has the discovery that you no longer love Andrew affected your feelings for Scott?" Elizabeth elaborated with remarkable patience.

Anna stared at her mother without really seeing her as Scott's lean, deeply tanned features swam before her eyes, and she muttered confusedly, "I . . . don't know."

The ringing of the telephone in the hall finally penetrated the ensuing silence, and Anna pulled herself together instantly at the terrified look that flashed across her mother's face when she said:

"I wonder who that can be at this time of night?"

"I'll take it, Mother," Anna said hastily, thankful to be doing something else instead of delving into her muddled thoughts to find a solution to the unexpected situation which had arisen in her life.

Controlling her own fears, she lifted the receiver, but as Scott's deep voice came clearly over the line, she asked him to wait a moment while she reassured her mother.

"I apologise if telephoning at this hour has given your

mother cause for alarm, but I arrived home only a short while ago," Scott explained when she returned to the telephone. "How is your father?"

"He's tired and weak, but the doctor thinks he might be well enough to return home within two weeks," she replied, hesitating momentarily before she added, "Scott – if you don't mind – I would like to stay on here until he leaves the hospital."

"Yes, of course," Scott agreed readily. "I'll come up to Johannesburg as soon as I can."

She thought of how often he had been away from home lately, and asked scathingly, "Are you sure you'll have the time?"

There was an electrifying pause before he said: "I detect something in that remark of yours which isn't very pleasant."

"I'm sorry," she apologised, filled with instant remorse. "Perhaps I'm just a little tired."

"I won't keep you, then," he said abruptly. "Give my regards to your mother ... and to your father when you see him again."

"Scott ..." she began hastily, reluctant to sever this unsatisfactory link with him for some inexplicable reason, but to her dismay she could find nothing to say.

"Yes?" he prompted.

"Nothing," she sighed helplessly. "Take care of yourself, and ... thank you for telephoning."

Take care of yourself. What on earth had possessed her to say that? she wondered confusedly as she heard Scott laugh softly at the other end.

"Goodnight, my love, and dream of me tonight," he said in that deep, caressing voice of his, and the line went dead before she could reply.

Anna replaced the receiver and was surprised to discover that she was shaking in every limb. With Scott's voice still ringing in her ears, and his tall, strong image conjured up in her mind, she realised the incredible and shattering truth.

"Anna?"

"Scott sends his regards," she said as she looked up to find her mother standing beside her, but she was only vaguely aware of what she was saying as she added, "He'll come as soon as he can."

Elizabeth Lindsay stared at her daughter curiously and muttered something about locking up. Anna reacted automatically to her mother's instructions as they locked the doors and went upstairs, but it was only in the privacy of her bedroom that she managed to put into words the feelings which seemed to cascade through her.

She loved Scott in a way she had never loved Andrew. It was difficult now to assess exactly what she had felt for Andrew at the time, but it certainly came nowhere near her feelings for Scott.

'Love is the master-key that opens every ward of the heart of man,' she recalled reading somewhere once, and suddenly it all made such wonderful sense. Andrew had merely succeeded in touching the outer walls of her heart, but Scott had somehow obtained the key to take complete possession without her even realising it.

Oh, what a *fool* she had been! she accused herself angrily. She should have known from the start that there was more to her feelings for Scott than just a mere physical attraction, but she had blindly believed that she could never love anyone else again.

She *had* to tell Scott. She had to let him know in some way how she felt. But how? She raised her hand tiredly and brushed her hair out of her eyes as she lowered herself on to the bed. When Scott had asked her to marry him, he had not asked her to love him as well, and during the weeks following their marriage he had never once indicated that he cared for her to that extent. Had the failure of his first marriage made him wary of loving someone again, or was it simply that he had no love to give? she wondered suddenly.

Anna struggled with her thoughts for quite some time after she had bathed and gone to bed, but she merely became more confused and unsure of herself as the minutes sped by.

"Oh, Scott, come soon," she whispered despairingly into the darkness. "Come soon so I can have some idea of how you really feel."

To everyone's relief, Charles Lindsay's condition improved rapidly during the next few days. Anna drove her mother to the hospital twice a day in her father's car, and as a result of this she saw very little of Andrew, which was a blessing in itself. Debbie came to the house a few times, but Anna found that they had very little to say to each other, and subsequently they avoided each other as much as possible.

Scott had telephoned almost every day to ask after her father, but their conversations had been brief and most unsatisfactory as far as Anna was concerned. He made no mention of coming to Johannesburg again, and somehow she had found it difficult to ask what his plans were.

Anna's mother was in her room when the telephone rang just after five on the Friday afternoon, and, leaving Debbie in the kitchen to see to the dinner, Anna hurried into the hall to answer it.

It was not Scott telephoning, as she had hoped, but Andrew, and Anna swallowed down her disappointment with difficulty.

"Anna, is Debbie there?"

"Yes, I'll –"

"No, wait!" Andrew stopped her urgently. "I told her I'd be working late," he went on to explain, and then he seemed to hesitate before he added, "Anna, I must see you alone."

"Are you crazy?" she demanded, lowering her voice automatically.

"It's important," Andrew insisted. "I *must* see you this evening."

"Where are you now?" she asked hesitantly.

"At the office," he told her. "Do you think you could slip away and have dinner with me somewhere?"

Anna's curiosity was dampened by a little voice that warned repeatedly against such a meeting, and she said quickly, "I don't think it would be wise."

"Please, Anna," he begged urgently. "It's vitally important."

If what Andrew wanted to discuss was of such vital importance, then it had to be something which would affect Debbie as well, Anna concluded, and, against her better judgement, she said: "Very well, then. Where shall I meet you?"

Andrew mentioned a restaurant they had often frequented over the years, and it was agreed that Anna should meet him there within an hour. Replacing the receiver, she telephoned for a taxi, and then, steeling herself, she returned to the kitchen to face her sister.

"Do you think you could drive Mother to the hospital in Daddy's car this evening?"

"Yes, of course," Debbie replied, looking faintly suspicious. "Are you going out?"

"I have to meet a friend of mine, and I might get back

too late to take Mother to the hospital myself," Anna explained, feeling more than just a little guilty as she met her sister's curious glance. "You don't mind, do you?"

"Not at all," Debbie assured her absently. "Shall we keep your dinner in the oven for you?"

"No, I'll have something to eat while I'm out." Anna hesitated in the doorway. "If I don't see Mother, will you explain the situation to her?"

Debbie nodded, and Anna fled upstairs to change into something more suitable than the slacks and sweater she was wearing, and she did so hurriedly before she changed her mind again about meeting Andrew.

Anna doubted the sensibility of her decision when she entered the restaurant an hour later and saw Andrew coming towards her, but it was too late now to do anything about it, she realised agitatedly.

"Anna!" he smiled, taking her arm and guiding her towards the table in the far corner where they had so often dined together during those years before Debbie had taken her place. Whether his choice had been intentional, or quite the opposite, no longer mattered to her as she faced him across the table with its checkered cloth. "I'm so glad you could make it," he said warmly as he stretched out a hand to clasp hers.

Anna stared at that thin, bony hand for a moment before sliding her hand from beneath it with a slight feeling of distaste.

"I'm not very happy about this meeting, Andrew," she told him a little sharply.

"Neither am I, but I couldn't think of any other way to see you alone," he explained, his dark eyes searching hers with a hint of anxiety in their depths. "You didn't tell your mother about this, did you?"

"I never saw my mother before leaving the house," she replied tritely. "The only one I spoke to was Debbie, and it was bad enough having to lie to her."

Their conversation was interrupted by the waiter wanting to take their order, and for almost an hour afterwards, while their dinner was served to them, Andrew thwarted her attempts to bring the conversation back to the reason for her presence there with him.

"All right, Andrew," she said eventually when their coffee had been served. "We've eaten a superb dinner, and we've explored every avenue of small talk while doing so. Don't you think it's time you told me what was so important that I simply had to meet you here?"

Andrew's eyes swept over her with a warmth that left her cold and untouched, but she was considerably shaken when he said: "Seeing you again has made me realise what a terrible mistake I made. I should have married *you*, Anna."

"I don't consider that a compliment," she said scornfully when she had recovered sufficiently. "You made your choice, and there's nothing I can, or want, to do about it now."

Andrew lowered his glance guiltily. "I treated you badly, and I don't blame you if you find it hard to forgive me."

Anna stared hard at him for endless seconds while she tried to discover what it was about him that had made her think that she had loved him. She had to admit that he was attractive, in a lean sort of way, but his chin was too weak, and his apparent inability to stick to the decision he had made did not count in his favour either. He had always been rather an undecided person, now she came to think of it, and she could not help comparing him with Scott who could be so forceful and determined when it came to the things he wanted. There was never any dilly-dallying with Scott. Once he had made up his mind, he sprang into action, and once he had made a decision he stuck to it.

"What happened between us is in the past, as far as I'm concerned," she said eventually. "You're married to Debbie, and I'm married to Scott. You'll just have to make the best of the situation, but whatever you do don't let Debbie down."

"About us, Anna –" he began, but she interrupted him hurriedly.

"Forget about us for the moment, Andrew, and tell me why you think that you made a mistake when you married Debbie."

"It's a little complicated," he prevaricated.

"I'm here now, and I'm willing to listen, so you might as well tell me," she insisted. "You were both very much in love when you decided to get married, weren't you?"

"Yes, we were," he admitted reluctantly. "But Debbie changed."

"Debbie changed?"

Andrew shifted uncomfortably in his chair. "Oh, well, I suppose I changed as well."

"Do you think you could be a little more explicit?" she asked, on the verge of losing her patience with him.

"Debbie changed from the loving, vivacious little creature she was, into a sullen, frigid woman," he explained at last, colouring a little when he met Anna's steady regard. "I've tried to talk to her, but it's no use. She can't give me an explanation for her behaviour, but she's certainly made me realise what a mistake I made. I gave up trying to understand her weeks ago, and the situation has just gone from bad to worse."

A problem of such a personal nature was best left to

the people concerned, Anna decided wisely and, as Andrew was obviously waiting for her to offer some sort of advice, she said quietly, "I'm afraid I can't help you, Andrew, but I do suggest that the two of you have a long talk in order to sort out your problems before it's too late to do anything about it."

"I feel so terribly guilty about the way I treated you," he stated unexpectedly.

"Guilty?" She stared at him in surprise. "Why on earth should you feel guilty?"

"I knew that you loved me, and it hit you hard when I decided to marry Debbie."

"I *thought* I loved you, Andrew," she corrected him quietly, meeting his incredulous gaze.

"What do you mean?" he demanded, flushing slightly.

"Just exactly that," she said a little abruptly. "I thought I loved you, and at the time I was shattered to learn that you were going to marry Debbie, but I realise now that it would have been a disaster if you and I had married each other."

Andrew looked momentarily stunned as he pushed an unsteady hand through his sandy hair. "Your feelings for me have changed, then?"

A cynical little smile played about her mouth. "Were you hoping I would still feel the same way about you?"

"No, but –" He gestured vaguely through the air. "I thought you might still care a little, at least."

"What purpose would that have served?"

"I don't know," he admitted thoughtfully, then his glance flickered over her, taking in the reddish-gold hair that fell in soft waves on to her shoulders, the creamy smoothness of her skin, and the hint of mockery about her faintly sensuous mouth. "You're very beautiful, Anna."

Anna stiffened involuntarily. "So my husband tells me."

"I should have married you."

"You had several years to make up your mind about that, but you chose to marry my sister instead," she reminded him sharply. "Be sensible, Andrew, and stop dithering. Don't imagine that you care for me in any way, because you don't. Give Debbie time until my father is home and on the mend, then discuss the problem with her. The solution lies between the two of you, and I wouldn't dream of interfering." He was behaving like an obstinate little boy, she decided as she glanced at her watch and noticed the time. "You'd better take me home now before Mother and Debbie return from the hospital and find you dropping me off at the house."

Andrew rose immediately and ushered her out to where he had parked his car, and neither of them made any attempt to break the silence during the drive out to Sandton. Anna's longing for Scott increased suddenly, and she longed, too, for the haven of his arms about her, but as they approached the house her thoughts returned to the discussion she had had with Andrew.

"Be honest with me, Andrew," she insisted when he had parked his car in the shadows close to the gate. "You still love Debbie, don't you?"

"Yes, I do, but at the moment –"

"Never mind how you feel at the moment," she silenced him impatiently. "Have you no idea at all what could have come between you?"

"If I knew that, I wouldn't be sitting here discussing my personal problems with you, would I?" he replied without hesitation, then he turned to face her, but his expression was hidden in the darkness. "I said some pretty ridiculous things this evening, and I apologise for them, but do you think you could talk some sense into Debbie?"

Anna shrank instantly from the idea. "Debbie and I have never been very close, Andrew, and I doubt if she would take kindly to any interference from me."

"It was just a suggestion," he muttered, and as she searched his face in the darkness of the car, sensing his attitude of utter despair, she found herself relenting.

"If the opportunity arises, then I'll try, Andrew, but I can't promise anything," she added hastily when he gripped her hands eagerly.

"I would be very grateful to you, Anna."

"I'd better go in," she said quickly, disengaging her hands and opening the door beside her. "Thank you for the dinner, and think very carefully before you do anything silly."

"I must thank you for coming when I needed you, Anna," he replied warmly as she left his car.

"Goodnight, Andrew," she said hurriedly, and, as his car sped down the street, she turned towards the gate, her hand fumbling impatiently with the catch before it swung open on its oiled hinges.

Anna paused momentarily when she noticed that the living-room lights had been left on, but when something moved in the shadows beside her she went rigid with fear. A paralysing numbness choked off the scream that rose in her throat, and it seemed as though an eternity passed before she recognised the man who stepped out on to the path directly in front of her.

"Scott!" his name spilled joyously from her lips as she clutched at him blindly, but his arms remained rigid and unresponsive at his sides. It was then that she noticed his tight-lipped expression in the dull glow of the street light, and her heart gave a sickening jolt when she realised that he must have been standing there in the shadows observing her while she had sat talking to Andrew in his car. The implications struck her forcibly like the blow of a sledge-hammer, and for some time she was too stunned to speak.

CHAPTER SEVEN

IT DID not require much ingenuity for Anna to realise that Scott could not have stood more than two metres away from her when she had left Andrew's car, and if he had been in any doubt as to the identity of her companion, then she herself had enlightened him by mentioning Andrew's name when she had bade him goodnight. She could imagine Scott's thoughts at that moment, and she groaned inwardly as she stared up into his chiselled, expressionless face, while her mind searched frantically for something to say which would break the uncomfortable and incredibly tense silence between them.

"Why didn't you let me know you'd be arriving this evening?" she said the first thing that came to mind, but she could have bitten off her tongue when she saw his lips twist into a harsh, cynical line.

"So you could have had time to arrange your *affairs* a little differently?" he suggested icily.

"Don't be silly, Scott."

"I understood from Debbie that her husband was working late at the office, and that you were meeting a friend," he went on in that unnaturally cold voice that sent shivers of fear up her spine. "It seems as though she was misinformed."

"Scott ... I can explain," she began desperately.

"I'm quite sure you can," he interrupted her harshly. "But I'm not so sure that I would care to hear it."

"It isn't —"

"I always credited you with honesty and integrity, Anna, but I've just been proved wrong, and I'm not finding the discovery very pleasant," he announced coldly, and it was like the thrust of a sword through her heart that made her flinch with pain.

"Scott, will you listen to me!"

"I suppose you're going to tell me that Andrew has finally discovered his mistake, and don't leave out the interesting part about how you were only too willing to console him."

Scott was so close to the truth — the slightly distorted truth — that she stared at him speechlessly for a moment before saying quietly, "It wasn't quite like that, Scott."

His heavy eyebrows rose sardonically. "You mean it's the other way round?"

"*No!*" she cried desperately, then, realising that they could not continue this conversation in the garden, she gestured towards the house. "Let's go inside."

Scott followed her into the house in silence, and when she turned to face him in the living-room her heart quickened its pace despite the coldness of those deep blue eyes which had so often caressed her with a glance. She had never desired his arms about her as much as she did at that moment. She wanted to cling to him and cry out her love for him against that broad, solid chest, but his unyielding attitude offered her no encouragement.

"Scott ..." she began in a choked voice, wanting desperately to make her feelings known to him. "Andrew means nothing to me any more."

"Really?" he mocked her cynically. "Are you going to

tell me now that you think you're in love with me?"

Anna flinched and the blood receded from her cheeks as Scott, without realising it, guessed at the truth, and she swallowed her defeat with difficulty. To confess her love for him after that scathing comment would only lay her wide open to his ridicule, and she could not bear that; not while her love for him was still something new and precious.

"Scott ..." she whispered his name, holding out her hands to him in an unconsciously pleading gesture, but she let them fall back lifelessly to her sides when he turned away from her and lit a cigarette.

"Don't try to make a fool of me, Anna," he said harshly with his broad back turned towards her. "When I met you, you were suffering from the after-effects of your unrequited love for Andrew Tait, and I was well aware of the fact that you still loved him when you married me. Don't make the situation worse now by trying to cover up the truth with more lies."

"I had no intention of lying to you, I –" She broke off abruptly as her anger flared, and, unable to face his formidable back a moment longer, she gripped his arm and turned him towards her. "Scott Beresford, you're the most obstinate, pigheaded man I've ever met!" she fumed up at him. "And I don't know why I –"

She stopped in mid-sentence at the sound of a car coming up the drive and, realising that she still clutched Scott's arms, she released him and drew a deep breath to steady herself.

"Please, Scott," she begged quietly. "For everyone's sake ... don't say anything?"

"If you're asking me to remain silent about your ... *affair*," he stressed the word sneeringly, "then you can rely on me not to mention the distasteful subject."

Anna flashed him an angry glance, but there was just enough time to compose herself before her mother and Debbie entered the living-room.

Scott behaved in his usual impeccable manner, and although no one appeared to notice it, he very cleverly excluded Anna from the conversation, and she finally gave up the effort to appear natural and went through to the kitchen to make the tea. She tried to shut her mind to what went on in the living-room, but, when the murmur of Scott's voice and Debbie's unconsciously provocative laughter blended so perfectly, she experienced an emotion she had always despised. Jealousy, like a white-hot fire, raced through her veins and blinded her momentarily. She was being ridiculous, she told herself, but right at that moment she could not tolerate it that Scott should behave so naturally with her sister and her mother, while *she* had to be satisfied with his cold, distrusting cynicism.

"You must have been surprised to find Scott waiting for you when you got back, Anna," her mother remarked unsuspectingly when there was a lull in the conversation after Anna had brought in the tea.

"Yes, it ... was a surprise," Anna replied haltingly, glancing swiftly at Scott, but he appeared to be intent upon lighting a cigarette. "How is Daddy this evening?" she changed the subject hastily.

"He's looking well, and impatient to come home, but the doctor insists that he should stay in hospital for another week."

Debbie rose with obvious reluctance at the sound of a car coming up the drive. "That will be Andrew, and I'd better not keep him waiting."

Scott was on his feet at once, towering over Debbie as he took her hand in his. "It's been delightful meeting you at last, Debbie."

"I'm so glad to have met you, too, Scott," Debbie smiled sweetly, melting with obvious delight beneath Scott's blue gaze, then she turned and kissed her mother lightly on the cheek. "Goodnight, Mom."

She nodded briefly in Anna's direction and left the room with Scott, who insisted on walking her to the door. Anna fumed inwardly, but as she became aware of her mother's curious glance resting on her, she busied herself with collecting the cups and carrying the tray through to the kitchen. Scott entered the house a few minutes later and she could hear him talking quietly to her mother in the living-room, but she deliberately lingered over the washing up of the cups in an effort to control her temper. She had to sort this problem out with Scott before they went to bed, she decided firmly. To leave it any longer would only create an unnecessary barrier between them, and that would be intolerable now that she knew how much she loved him.

Her opportunity came when Scott emerged from the shower and walked across to the bed. She sat up instantly against the pillows, her heart pounding wildly at the sight of him in his brown, silk dressing gown, and her thoughts returned inevitably to that first night of their marriage. He had come to her then wearing that same dressing gown, and she had been excited and afraid, simultaneously, by his masculinity.

"Scott . . ." she began hesitantly as he sat down on the edge of the bed with his back turned firmly towards her. "Could we talk quietly and sensibly for a few minutes?"

"I don't think there's anything that needs discussing, Anna," he contradicted harshly. "I'm trying my best to understand what you must be going through after seeing Andrew again, but let's not dissect the incident further."

It was clear to her that Scott was convinced that she still cared for Andrew and, in her urgency to make him realise the truth, she leaned forward and felt the muscles grow taut in his arm when she touched him.

"I wish you'd let me explain."

He brushed off her hand distastefully. "The subject is closed, Anna, and I don't want it mentioned again."

Her eyes clouded with pain as she watched him slip out of his robe and climb into bed. He made no attempt to lie closer to her when he had switched off his bedside light and, switching off her own, she remained on her side of the bed, staring into the darkness with a heaviness in her breast which was born of despair.

She had longed for Scott to come to her and, now that he was there, everything had gone wrong. If she could have turned back the clock a few hours to the time Andrew had telephoned her, then she would have heeded the warnings of that wise little voice, and everything would have been so different.

What a futile thought! she realised angrily, and for the first time in many months she felt the hot tears filling her eyes and spilling over on to her cheeks.

Anna slept fitfully that night as the agony of having Scott so close, and yet so far, gnawed away at her. It hurt that not even in his sleep had he attempted to touch her, and her heart felt like a lead weight in her chest when she awoke the following morning to find he had already dressed and gone down to have breakfast. Pulling on a pair of slacks and a blouse, she hurried down to join him, hoping to find him in a more receptive mood, but he informed her curtly that he had business to attend to in the city, and left the house a few minutes later without so much as glancing at her.

Anna had not questioned the validity of his statement,

but she spent the rest of the morning brooding over his unrelenting attitude, and when he finally returned to the house just before lunch, she had made up her mind to return home with him that Saturday afternoon.

"What the devil do you think you're doing?" he demanded when he found her up in the bedroom packing her suitcase.

"I've decided to return home with you," she replied quite clearly without looking up from her task. "I don't think I'll have any difficulty getting a seat on the same flight."

"You're doing nothing of the sort!" he snapped, and he was beside her in one stride, tilting the contents of her suitcase out on to the bed. "You're staying here as planned, until your father comes out of hospital."

"But, Scott –"

"You're staying!"

His voice had the effect of a whiplash, and it frightened her into submission as he towered over her menacingly.

"If that's what you really want, then I suppose I shall have to stay," she said unsteadily, shrinking inwardly at the pent-up fury in his eyes.

"That's what I want," he stated decisively, and moments later she was alone and feeling peculiarly like a child who had just been severely punished.

The situation between them became almost intolerable as the afternoon progressed, and Anna marvelled at her own ability to withstand the strain and tension of having to appear normal before the rest of the family.

Her nerves were severely tested, however, when they arrived at the hospital that afternoon. Scott, his face an inscrutable mask, came face to face with Andrew for the first time, and Anna somehow made the introductions without faltering. It was a devilish situation, and one which she would have given anything to avoid at that precise moment, but this meeting between them was inevitable, and there was nothing she could do to alter the circumstances.

Anna skilfully avoided Andrew's curiously questioning glances by giving her father her undivided attention as they stood around his bed, but her relief was intense when the visiting hour was finally over and they could take their leave.

Her hands were clammy when they stepped out of the clinical building and into the sunshine, but her legs felt as though they wanted to cave in beneath her when her mother asked Debbie and Andrew to join them for tea at the house. Anna steadied herself against the bonnet of her father's car as she summoned up the strength to continue with the charade, but Andrew declined the invitation and hastily marched Debbie off to where he had parked his car.

Anna closed her eyes and could have wept with relief, but she pulled herself together and climbed into the car before her mother or Scott noticed the faint shimmering of unwanted tears in her eyes.

Scott had arranged to return to Durban on the early evening flight, and Anna followed him diffidently when he eventually excused himself and went upstairs to collect his things.

"I'll drive you out to the airport," she offered nervously as she stood aside and watched him applying pressure to the lid of his case and fastening the catches.

"I'll get a taxi," he replied without looking up from his task.

"Don't be so infuriatingly self-sufficient, Scott," she sighed in exasperation. "You won't let me go home with you, but you can at least accept my offer and allow me to drive you to the airport."

Scott straightened then with a cynical expression marring his attractive features and, despite her own tallness, he seemed to tower over her. "Is this some sort of olive branch you're offering me?"

Anna considered she had done remarkably well in keeping her temper in check, but her control snapped for some reason, and she reacted in a way she had never done before. Her hand flew up to strike him, but his fingers latched on to her wrist while it was still in mid-air, and he gave her arm a painful twist that made her cry out in agony.

"Don't ever try that again," he warned in a voice that was dangerously calm as he released her. "I may surprise you by retaliating in a similar, but more painful fashion."

She had no idea what had possessed her to behave so despicably, but, as she turned away to hide her tears of despair, she realised that she had deserved his cruelty.

"I'm sorry," she murmured unsteadily as she fought to regain the control she had lost so completely, and there was a tense, frightening little silence before she heard him speak.

"If you're going to drive me out to Jan Smuts, then we'd better go."

His statement was such an anti-climax that she had to choke back a wave of hysteria before she could trust her voice to sound normal.

"I'll get the car keys," she managed eventually, and escaped before he could change his mind.

Anna waited in the car while Scott bade her mother farewell, but from the moment he slid into the seat beside her she became aware of the ever-widening gulf between them. His hostility towards her was something she could not bear, and during the drive out to the airport she became frustrated by her helpless inability to do anything about it.

"Let me know when to expect you so I can arrange *my* plans accordingly," he remarked scathingly as they waited in the departure lounge for his flight to be called.

"Don't, Scott,' she pleaded, wincing inwardly as his words found their mark like a well-aimed arrow. "Don't create something out of nothing."

"Do you expect me to overlook the fact that you had a secret assignation with your sister's husband because you're still in love with him?" he demanded tersely, his eyes raking her insultingly from head to foot until her cheeks were flushed with humiliation.

"I don't expect you to overlook anything," she argued quietly, her hands gripping the edge of her seat. "All I ask for is the chance to explain what happened. I didn't —"

A melodious female voice over the intercom system cut across her intended explanation and brought Scott to his feet.

"That's my flight number."

Anna stood up jerkily, her heart beating painfully against her ribs as they stood facing each other. The flight announcement had defeated her attempt to vindicate herself, and had his attitude not been so forbidding, she would have done almost anything at that moment to keep him there with her.

"Aren't you going to kiss me before you go?" she asked a little audaciously, determined not to be intimidated by him.

He raised one cynical eyebrow and said impatiently, "Yes, if you really want me to."

His kiss was cold and impersonal but, as he was about to move away from her, she clutched at him in frantic desperation.

"Scott, please ..." she begged, her mouth quivering uncontrollably and her eyes brimming with unashamed tears, but he remained curiously unmoved as he brushed aside her hands and stepped back.

"Goodbye, Anna."

She stared after him, her tears distorting his tall, imposing figure as he strode towards the departure gate without looking back. She wanted to run after him, to beg him to stay, or to take her with him. *Anything* would be preferable to having to part from him, she decided, but she seemed incapable of moving as she recalled his parting words.

Goodbye, Anna. Recalling it now made it sound so dreadfully final that she shook uncontrollably as she made her way back to the car. Had Scott perhaps tried to convey something to her which she was too frightened and confused to grasp, or was she merely allowing her imagination to get the better of her?

Goodbye, Anna. The words reverberated through her tortured mind as she drove back to Sandton, and it was something close to a miracle that she arrived safely at her destination, for she had very little recollection afterwards of where and how she had travelled.

The week following Scott's departure seemed to pass with agonising slowness, and if Anna had not promised her father that she would remain with her mother for the duration of his stay in hospital, she would have returned to Amazibu Bay soon after Scott. He telephoned regularly for news of Charles, but his hostile and distant attitude did nothing to restore Anna's confidence, and she found herself becoming increasingly impatient to return home. It had become vitally important to her that she should erase the barrier which had been erected between them, and she *had* to make him understand somehow that Andrew no longer meant anything to her.

Charles Lindsay was allowed home the following Saturday, and although he complained about the room they had prepared for him on the ground floor, he finally admitted that it would be some time before he would be strong enough to negotiate the stairs. Elizabeth settled him into a comfortable chair in the living-room, and fussed over him like a hen with one chick, and despite her father's protests, Anna suspected that he secretly relished all the attention he was receiving.

Anna shelved her own problems momentarily as she noticed the signs of strain on Debbie's face when she and Andrew joined them for lunch on the Sunday. They seemed to be in no hurry to return to their apartment afterwards, and when Anna finally went through to the kitchen to make tea that afternoon, she was surprised to see her sister get up and follow her from the room. Anna was instantly on her guard, for it was the first time Debbie had deliberately sought out her company, and that in itself was unusual.

She observed her sister unobtrusively, noticing how she fidgeted with the sugar bowl and the cups as if she couldn't quite make up her mind about something, and several nerve-racking seconds passed before she seemed to pluck up the courage to speak.

"Anna ..." she began self-consciously, digging the spoon into the sugar like someone digging for treasure. "About you and Scott ..."

Wariness made Anna stiffen. "What about us?"

Debbie's grey glance was troubled and questioning. "You are happy, aren't you?"

"Shouldn't we be?" Anna demanded guardedly.

"Don't be so evasive, Anna ... please! I *must* know," Debbie insisted, her voice low and urgent. "Don't you realise that I wouldn't be prying into your personal life like this if it wasn't important?"

Anna would have had to be totally obtuse not to suspect that this might have something to do with the conversation she had had with Andrew, and she sounded a little more encouraging as she said carefully, "If you could explain why it's so important for you to know whether Scott and I are happy, then I might begin to understand."

Debbie relinquished her treasure-digging activities in the sugar bowl to clutch at the back of a kitchen chair until her knuckles showed white, then she whispered urgently, "Anna, I can't live with this terrible feeling of guilt much longer. I may have given the impression that I'm totally insensitive, but I'm being destroyed by guilt!"

"Guilt, Debbie?"

"Yes," Debbie nodded, her facial muscles twitching nervously. "We – Andrew and I – we hurt you very much, didn't we?"

"At that time I was hurt very deeply, yes, but there's no need for you to feel guilty about it," Anna assured her as she switched off the kettle and gave her sister her undivided attention. "Debbie ... Andrew and I would never have been happy together, because I know now that I never really cared for him."

"You do love Scott, then?"

Anna found it difficult voicing the answer to such a personal question, but knowing that Debbie's happiness depended on it, she said: "Yes ... very much."

"Oh, Anna," Debbie sighed, her lips trembling as she fought against the tears. "You don't know what a relief it is to hear you say that!"

"This guilt you spoke of, Debbie," Anna began, feeling closer to her sister at that moment than they had ever been before. "Has it affected your relationship with Andrew in any way?"

"Yes, it has, I'm afraid," Debbie admitted, biting her lip nervously. "I love him, Anna, I really do. I've tried my best to be the kind of wife he wanted, but every time he touches me, I —"

"You are overcome with unnecessary guilt?" Anna filled in for her when she hesitated.

"Yes." Debbie brushed a strand of silky fair hair out of her eyes and turned to stare out of the window. "It's reached the stage now where I'm beginning to think I've killed every scrap of love he had for me."

"I don't think that's possible," Anna assured her gently.

"What am I going to do, Anna?" her sister wanted to know with a note of despair in her voice. "Mother has always said that you're such a sensible person, and I desperately need advice."

Anna was not so sure that she was as sensible as they imagined her to be when she thought of the problems that awaited her at Amazibu Bay, but keeping in mind her conversation with Andrew on that fateful evening, and her promise to help in some way, she said: "There's no need for you to feel guilty about anything in future, and if it means that you have to make the first move towards restoring your marriage, then make that move, and make it soon. Give Andrew some indication that you've shaken off this phobia of yours, and the rest will come naturally."

"Do you really think so?" Debbie asked dubiously.

"I'm positive it will work."

Footsteps echoed down the passage towards the kitchen, and Debbie turned away hastily to remove the evidence of her recent tears, barely succeeding in regaining her composure before Andrew walked through the door.

"What are you two nattering about?" he demanded playfully. "Where's that tea we were promised?"

"The tea will be ready in a few minutes," Anna promised hastily, her eyes issuing a silent instruction at Debbie which her sister reacted upon after a moment of uncertainty.

"Andrew," she began, taking his hands and drawing him towards the door leading into the back garden. "Will you come with me for a moment, please?"

Andrew shot a curious glance at Anna, but followed Debbie into the garden without protesting, and Anna watched them through the window until they disappeared into the old summer-house.

Anna delayed the tea for several minutes before she carried the tray through to the living-room, and there was a lump in her throat when Debbie and Andrew eventually joined them there. They were holding hands like young lovers, while their expressions suggested that they had succeeded in reaching a new understanding, and Anna hoped fervently that she would have as much success with Scott when she returned home.

Anna discussed her plans with her parents that evening, and made arrangements the following morning for her flight to Durban that same afternoon. All that remained was for Scott to be informed of her time of arrival, but when she telephoned Amazibu Bay she found only his aunt at home.

"Scott said he would be home for lunch," Aunt Dorrie explained. "I'll give him your message as soon as he arrives." She asked after Charles Lindsay's health, and then added, "I'm so glad you're coming home at last, Anna."

Dorothy MacPherson's voice had sounded odd, Anna thought frowningly as she replaced the receiver. Could it be that something had happened of which she was as yet unaware? Something to do with Scott, perhaps?

"It's my imagination again," Anna told herself finally when she was unable to find an answer, and she hurried up to her room to fling the last few things into her suitcase.

She could no longer curb her impatience to be with Scott, and when the plane finally landed at the Durban airport that afternoon she felt decidedly faint with excitement. Scott was there to meet her, and her enthusiasm would have sent her rushing headlong into his arms if the austerity of his expression had not forbidden it so absolutely. Surely he was not still bearing a grudge because she had spent those few hours alone with Andrew? she thought irritably as he collected her suitcase in silence and hurried her out to the car.

Their conversation was polite and strained while Scott negotiated the Mercedes from the airport grounds, but, as he took the road south to Amazibu Bay, Anna threw all caution to the winds.

"Scott, you're not still angry with me, are you?" she demanded evenly as she glanced at his stern profile and saw nothing there which offered encouragement.

"I was never angry with you, Anna."

"No, you were furious," she amended with a faintly amused smile. "You were furious because you saw me with Andrew, but —"

"That's enough!" he interrupted harshly, his hands clenching the steering wheel as if he wanted to snap it in two. "I told you the subject was closed."

"I never considered you to be an unreasonable man, Scott," she said at length, staring blindly ahead of her and seeing nothing of the lush, subtropical greenery along the coastal drive. "I credited you with a little more intelligence and understanding."

"I've a lot of important matters on my mind at the moment, Anna," he said coldly, "and I really can't be bothered with trivialities such as this."

"Trivialities!" she gasped incredulously, turning in her seat to stare at him. "Do you know what you're saying?"

"Yes," he smiled cynically. "I like to get my priorities in the correct order, and at the moment business comes before all else."

"I'm beginning to think the only thing that will ever be of any importance to you is your business!" she hit back at him in her state of frenzied unhappiness.

"You're quite right," he agreed bluntly.

Anna drew a careful, steadying breath. "And where exactly do I fit into this programme?"

He glanced at her briefly, but his expression gave nothing away. "You're my wife, of course, and as such you play quite a large role in my business affairs."

"I do?" she asked with a hint of mockery in her voice.

"You're forgetting that you're a twenty-five per cent shareholder in the business."

"I never asked you to make me a shareholder," she reminded him as she flinched inwardly and tried again. "Oh, Scott, this is all so unnecessary. We're saying things we don't mean and tearing each other apart in the process."

"I think we both know now exactly where we stand," he remarked coldly without taking his eyes off the road, and Anna felt a shiver of apprehension rippling through her.

"What's that supposed to mean?" she asked quietly.

"Just whatever you want to make of it," he stated bluntly, and Anna lapsed into a disturbed silence as she grapled with her turbulent thoughts.

Scott was so far removed from her at that moment that they could just as well have been sitting at the opposite ends of the earth instead of beside each other in the Mercedes, she thought dismally, and it seemed there was very little she could do about the situation, except wait, and hope that time would eliminate the friction between them.

Aunt Dorrie had a long, cool drink awaiting them on the terrace when they arrived, but Scott declined the invitation to join them, and left almost at once.

"I don't know what's got into that nephew of mine lately," Aunt Dorrie remarked as Anna handed her suitcase over to one of the servants to take up to her room. "He's been quite impossible this last week," she added as she waved Anna into a chair and placed a glass of chilled orange juice on the table beside her.

"Did anything of interest happen while I was away?" Anna asked, steering the conversation in a different direction.

"Something happened, all right," Aunt Dorrie replied instantly, her lips tightening ominously. "Joan Mulder is back."

At any other time this news would not have troubled Anna, but with the existing relationship between Scott and herself as it was, she could not prevent the flicker of anxiety that raced through her.

Making an effort to hide her fears, she asked casually, "When did she arrive?"

"She arrived a few days after you'd left for Johannesburg, and she's out to make mischief, if you ask me," Scott's aunt stated firmly.

Was it possible, Anna wondered silently, that Joan's return had something to do with Scott's unrelenting attitude? Was his anger at seeing her with Andrew merely an excuse to cover up his own preoccupation with Joan? It was a possibility she did not want to dwell on, but it was one she could not overlook, she decided unhappily.

"Have you seen her?" Anna continued to question Scott's aunt.

"No, I haven't, but news gets around very quickly in a small town like this," Aunt Dorrie replied with a slight grimace.

"Is her husband with her?"

"No," Aunt Dorrie shook her grey head and frowned. "And that's something else that troubles me. I've heard a rumour that they're in the process of divorcing each other."

"Has Scott seen her, do you think?" Anna asked cautiously, trying to ignore her rapidly increasing pangs of anxiety.

"I wouldn't know," the older woman replied thoughtfully. "He hasn't said a word, and he hasn't been in the right sort of mood for me to question him about it."

"I wonder . . ." Anna murmured, sipping at her orange juice as she stared out across the sunlit garden.

"What do you wonder, my dear?"

Anna hesitated momentarily before voicing her troubled thoughts. "I wonder if she's hoping to win Scott from me somehow."

"Don't be silly, Anna," Aunt Dorrie scolded her at once. "Besides, it's rather too late for that, don't you agree?"

"Yes," Anna replied distractedly. But was it too late? Would she be able to stand in his way if he made it clear that he preferred Joan after all?

"Do you think her return may have something to do with Scott's peculiar behaviour lately?" Aunt Dorrie interrupted the flow of Anna's frantic thoughts.

"I don't know," she replied evasively. "I'm certain, though, that he must know that she's here. Joan Mulder wouldn't waste much time in making sure that Scott was informed in some way or another."

"Oh, dear!" the older woman sighed heavily as she collected their empty glasses and placed them on the tray. "I do hope she has the sense not to upset everything again."

They were most probably making something out of nothing, Anna decided in a valiant effort to be sensible, but there was no harm in being prepared for whatever might eventuate in the future.

CHAPTER EIGHT

Scott returned home in time for dinner that evening, but instead of joining Anna on the terrace as he had always done in the past, he went upstairs directly to shower and change, and although every part of her cried out for her to go after him, she decided against it. At the dinner table Aunt Dorrie did most of the talking, seemingly oblivious of the strained atmosphere which existed between Scott and Anna.

"The annual Mayor's Ball is being held at the Tom-Tom this coming Friday evening," Scott addressed Anna directly for the first time as they were about to leave the table, and his cold glance flickered over her briefly as he added, "It's expected that we should attend."

He strode from the dining-room without giving her the opportunity to speak, and Anna stared after him thoughtfully until she heard the study door close behind him.

"What did Scott mean by saying it's expected that we should attend?" she asked Aunt Dorrie as she followed her into the living-room.

"The Mayor's Ball is always held at the Tom-Tom," Aunt Dorrie explained, seating herself in her favourite armchair and picking up her embroidery. "As he's the owner of the hotel it's naturally expected that Scott will attend."

Anna was not too sure whether she wanted to accompany Scott to the Ball while their relationship left so much to be desired, but as his aunt continued to elaborate on this annual function, Anna realised that it would look decidedly odd if Scott arrived at the Ball on his own.

Aunt Dorrie retired to bed early, as was her custom, and Anna followed her upstairs soon afterwards. It was a hot, humid night, and she took a cool shower before going to bed, but she found she was unable to sleep. She tossed and turned restlessly until she heard Scott enter the dressing-room through the passage entrance, and her heart thumped heavily against her ribs as she waited for him to join her, but the minutes passed and, to her dismay, she heard the springs of the bed in the dressing-room creaking beneath his weight.

Her first instinct was to go to him, to show him, in the only way she knew of, that she cared, but fear of being rejected left her lying rigid in the enormous bed with tears of frustration and disappointment gathering in her eyes. She tried to be sensible about it all, but the tears continued to pave their way down her cheeks, and the only thought that kept recurring was that she had ruined her only chance of happiness by being concerned for someone she no longer cared about.

Anna moved about restlessly beneath the sheets and shivered despite the fact that she was perspiring freely. She knew the symptoms only too well and, going through to the bathroom, she searched for the bottle of sleeping capsules she had hidden away somewhere in the back of the small cupboard. For the first time in months she needed to take something in order to escape for a few hours from the painful reality of life. It was the coward's way out, she recalled Sheila telling her once when Sheila had come into her bedroom unexpectedly to find her swallowing down the small capsule. She had relinquished the habit after that, but, just for this one night, she was going to be a coward once more, she decided as she swallowed down the capsule and returned to bed.

Her futile thoughts rotated madly through her mind before the harmless capsule took effect, but one clear thought remained to taunt her. If Scott had given her the opportunity to explain about Andrew, she would have found it virtually impossible to do so without confessing her feelings for him in the process. Scott had offered her marriage, not *love*, and if she had been foolish enough to fall in love with him, then she had only herself to blame. Scott's love was something she could not hope to possess, and now that he no longer shared the same room with her, she could not hope to expect much from their marriage either, unless she managed to convince him in some way of her fidelity.

She whispered his name involuntarily and yawned, and seconds later she slipped into a dreamless sleep from which she did not awake until long after breakfast the following morning.

Two days after her return from Johannesburg, Anna

answered the front door to find a familiar face standing before her. Her auburn hair was styled in a sleek silk cap about her head, and her dark, heavily mascaraed eyes surveyed Anna contemptuously.

"You're still here, then."

Acting on a great deal of supposition and a little of what Aunt Dorrie had told her, Anna schooled her voice and said with equal politeness, "Yes, thank you."

"How clever of you," the other woman smiled, but the hint of sarcasm in her melodious voice placed Anna instantly on her guard. "May I come in?"

"Please do," Anna murmured, and the curvacious figure, clad in pale gold chiffon, swept past her, leaving Anna to follow in the wake of her expensive perfume.

Joan lowered herself elegantly into the padded armchair beside the potted fern and glanced about her with a faintly cynical expression hovering about her full red mouth. "You've been making changes. I must admit I liked it better the way it was before."

Anna chose to ignore that remark as she sat down in the chair facing Joan and, deciding that the preliminaries had been dealt with sufficiently, she asked, "May I know the purpose of your visit?"

"I was hoping to see Scott," Joan replied without hesitation, her glance challenging Anna. "Is he at home?"

"I'm afraid Scott isn't in at the moment."

"When do you expect him back?"

"Not before this evening." Anna hesitated momentarily, angered by Joan's audacity, yet curious to know the reason for her desire to see Scott. "Was there something I could do for you, perhaps?"

"I shouldn't think so," Joan smiled sweetly. "What I have to discuss with Scott is of a personal nature."

Anna bit back the angry words that sprang to her

lips, and asked instead, "Does Scott know of your return to Amazibu Bay?"

"Yes, of course." A smile of satisfaction hovered about her lips as she crossed one shapely leg over the other. "Didn't he tell you?"

Anna controlled her features with difficulty as she explained. "I've been in Johannesburg these past two weeks, and we haven't really had much time to discuss anything since my return "

Joan offered Anna a cigarette but, when Anna declined, she selected one and placed it in a gold holder. She took her time about lighting it, and Anna made use of the opportunity to observe her more closely. Her skin was flawless, but slightly sallow, Anna noticed, and although there was remarkable beauty in the high cheekbones and perfectly shaped jaw, there was a calculating hardness in those heavily lashed eyes that did not appeal to Anna.

"I suppose that, considering the way news gets around in this place, you must have heard that I'm divorcing my husband?" Joan demanded, observing Anna through a screen of smoke.

"Yes, I've heard," Anna admitted warily.

Joan drew hard on her cigarette and her eyes narrowed slightly as she expelled another cloud of smoke into the air. "My marriage to Dennis was a mistake and you might as well know the truth – I intend to have Scott back."

Her bald statement jolted Anna physically and mentally, but she somehow managed to convey a cool, unruffled appearance. "That's rather presumptuous of you, isn't it?"

"I don't think so," Joan smiled with infuriating sweetness. "I've always believed in making my intentions quite clear to everyone. That way there can be no mis-understandings, don't you agree?"

The melodious voice which Anna had initially found so attractive now began to jar as she replied with equal frankness, "I think you're forgetting that Scott is now married to me, Joan, and I don't intend to hand him over to you as meekly as you may think."

"Scott loved me once and he'll love me again. There would be nothing you could do to prevent him from gaining his freedom if he desires it," Joan informed her chillingly. "He only dropped me when he married Trudie. Now I've ditched Dennis, I can assure you it won't be at all difficult to get him back."

Joan's statement had a ring of truth to it that was like the painful thrust of a knife. Pride, however, made Anna conceal her doubts from this woman who had now become her adversary, and, thinking of the relationship which had existed between Scott and herself before that unfortunate incident in Johannesburg, she somehow found the courage to say calmly,

"I wouldn't be too confident about your plans succeeding, if I were you, Joan."

The other woman extinguished her cigarette agitatedly and dropped the holder into her bag. "Don't think that because Scott made you a twenty-five per cent share-holder in his business you have some sort of hold over him, because you don't."

"I don't know how you found out about the interest I have in Scott's business, and I don't really care," Anna said coldly, barely able to conceal her surprise and distaste. "The hold I have over Scott is something much more personal, and totally beyond your understanding."

How could Anna explain to someone like Joan the joy she and Scott had found in each other's company?

Physically and intellectually they had complemented and stimulated each other in a manner which Joan would never understand. Trudie's lack of interest in Scott's business affairs alone had created a void between them which had resulted in her leaving him for another man. Joan was the same. The only thing she ever *would* be interested in was herself, Anna decided firmly.

"You're not expecting a child, are you?" Joan's voice cut across Anna's thoughts, and Anna stared at her blankly for a few startled seconds before she realised that Joan had misinterpreted her statement completely.

"Would that be so surprising?" Anna asked calmly, grasping at the weapon which Joan had inadvertently placed in her hands. "We *are* married, you know."

Joan was obviously shaken, Anna noticed with a flicker of satisfaction, but she rallied swiftly. "Scott wouldn't let something like that stand in his way when it comes to his feelings for me."

"Can you be sure of that?" Anna challenged her mockingly.

Joan paled visibly and jumped to her feet, her voice now shrill with agitation and dislike as she accused Anna. "You think you're very clever, don't you!"

Anna stood up as well and found that she had the advantage of a few centimetres over the other woman as she began to lodge her attack with a calmness that surprised even herself.

"I don't consider myself clever, Joan, but I do have my practical and sensible moments, and I don't take kindly to having my personal happiness threatened by someone as irresolute and insensitive as yourself."

"How dare you speak to me like that!" Joan snapped.

"How dare *you* think you can intimidate me into handing Scott over to you as if he were a misplaced parcel!" Anna countered swiftly, no longer making an effort to control her anger. "You had him once, but he left you in favour of someone else. Scott is married to *me* now, and I can promise you I won't be shaken off as easily as you may think."

"We shall see about that!" Joan shouted, and her lack of control was unpleasant to witness, for her beautiful face was distorted with fury. "Be warned, Anna. I'm now more determined than ever to do everything in my power to get him back, and I mean to succeed!"

The front door slammed behind her a few seconds later, and Anna observed her departure from the window as her chiffon-clad figure walked stiffly and erectly down the avenue of palms towards the large iron gates. She intended to make trouble, that much was obvious, Anna realised with a feeling of uneasiness, but would she succeed as she had so confidently claimed that she would?

"I must say you handled that very nicely, Anna."

Anna swung round in surprise to see Dorothy Mac-Pherson entering the living-room through the glass doors which opened out on to the terrace. "You heard?"

"I was on my way inside when I realised that you had company, and I couldn't help listening in on the conversation." Aunt Dorrie smiled a little self-consciously as she sniffed at the early summer roses she held in her hands. "Shameless of me, wasn't it."

"Not really," Anna assured her, her lips curving into an answering smile as the tension inside of her eased a little.

"It seemed to me that Joan was of the opinion that she could walk all over you much the same as she's always done with everyone else, and she was considerably shaken when she discovered you had no intention of letting her have her way." Aunt Dorrie laughed merrily, her eyes

crinkling up at the corners as she pushed the roses unceremoniously into a vase containing a few white daisies.
"She was silent for such a long time, after discovering
that you were expecting a child, that I thought for a
moment she had fainted."

"If you remember correctly, Aunt Dorrie, I never told
her I was pregnant," Anna hastened to correct her with
a feeling of guilt. "She jumped to the wrong conclusion,
and I'm ashamed to admit I decided not to contradict
her."

Aunt Dorrie's expression sobered instantly. "You
mean that you're not going to have a baby?"

"No, I'm not," Anna admitted, colouring slightly.
"Joan declared war, and in this kind of battle one uses
whatever weapons one can lay one's hands on, but my
only regret is that my weapon wasn't authentic."

"I must admit I'm a little disappointed. It's about
time this enormous house was filled with the laughter of
children echoing along the passages. But you're right, of
course," Aunt Dorrie announced, drawing Anna down
on to the sofa beside her. "She wouldn't hesitate to make
use of every foul method available to her, and you have
to defend yourself in some way." Mischief gleamed in the
depth of those blue eyes that were so very like Scott's.
"I thoroughly enjoyed it, though, when you did the at-
tacking, and Joan found herself on the defensive. It was
most probably the first time in her life she'd ever found
herself in that position, and it served her right."

Anna shook her head sadly. "I'm ashamed of myself."

"Don't be silly," the older woman argued. "What you
told her was the truth, and if Scott were here –"

"He would most probably have handled the situation
quite differently. In fact," Anne hesitated, glancing down
at her hands clenched so tightly in her lap, "the con-

versation between Joan and myself wouldn't have taken place at all if Scott had been here, and I'm beginning to wish he *had* been here to speak to her."

"Nonsense!" Aunt Dorrie's voice was almost a rebuke. "Don't you realise that you now have the advantage of knowing exactly what she's up to?"

"I wonder," Anna murmured, not sure whether anyone would ever know exactly what someone like Joan Mulder would do, and with the situation between Scott and herself as precarious as it was, there was no knowing how well Joan would succeed in her campaign to win Scott back.

"Scott would never tolerate her interference in your marriage," Aunt Dorrie remarked almost as if she had read Anna's thoughts.

Anna's smile was tinged with uncertainty. "I hope you're right, Aunt Dorrie."

Her meeting with Joan that morning, and their subsequent conversation, plagued Anna throughout the rest of the day. She tried to work off the uncertainty of her thoughts in the garden, but the heat finally drove her into the air-conditioned interior of the house.

She tried to rest after lunch, but instead she found herself pacing the floor of her bedroom as the silence in the house became oppressive. She wrestled endlessly with her thoughts until it felt as though her head would burst and, pulling the curtains aside, she stared out of the window. The almost deserted stretch of sandy beach beckoned to her invitingly and, making up her mind swiftly, she stripped and put on her bikini. With her towelling robe tied firmly about her waist, she pushed her feet into a pair of old sandals and went downstairs to leave a message for Aunt Dorrie on the hall table before hurrying from the house.

Anna reached the beach within a few minutes and, slipping out of her robe, she dropped it on to the sand beside her sandals. The sea looked deliciously cool, and she ran towards it, gasping a little as her heated body struck the water. Against Scott's repeated warnings, she swam out some distance before turning over on to her back and closing her eyes against the sun.

She drifted on the leisurely swell of the ocean, relaxing for the first time that day, and quite oblivious of how much time had elapsed before she eventually became aware of a difference in the motion of the sea beneath her. Her eyes flew open, and she caught her breath in alarm when she realised that the current had carried her a considerable distance from the shore.

Telling herself not to panic, she struck out towards the beach, but although she was a reasonably strong swimmer, she seemed to make no progress at all. The current was too strong for her, and her strength was ebbing swiftly. She dared not relax her efforts for one moment, Anna realised helplessly, but to continue swimming against such odds would finally result in her drowning from sheer exhaustion. The salt in her tears mingled with the salt of the sea as she cursed herself for her foolishness and, choking back a sob, she made a renewed and desperate effort to reach the shore.

Exhaustion finally claimed her, and she went down several times as though her body had been filled with lead. Each time she struggled weakly to the surface to drag the life-giving air painfully into her lungs, but there was an unfamiliar roaring in her ears, and a darkness that threatened to envelope her.

Something touched her thigh at this point, and alarm slicked through her like a blade of a knife. *Shark!* she thought and, panic-stricken, she lashed out blindly at the dark object beside her. She felt herself being lifted until her head was above the water and, drawing great gulps of air into her lungs, she continued her frenzied fight for survival.

"Stop that at once!" a familiar voice snapped, and then she thankfully knew nothing more until the sea seemed to spit them out on to the sandy beach.

"What a damn idiotic thing to do!" Scott accused harshly the moment he regained his breath. "Were you trying to drown yourself?"

"No," Anna coughed and spluttered, struggling weakly to her knees in the shallow water in order to brush her hair out of her eyes. "I underestimated the sea currents, that's all."

Scott's hands clamped about her upper arms like vices and she was lifted to her feet unceremoniously to be shaken until she hung limply like a rag doll in his grip, her teeth biting into her lower lip in an effort not to cry out against the pain.

"You've been warned repeatedly about not going in too far, and do you realise that if Aunt Dorrie hadn't become so concerned about you I might not have arrived in time to save you?" he demanded harshly as he shook her again with renewed vigour until it felt as though her neck would snap.

"Yes – and I'm sorry – but don't shout at me, and – and I wish you'd l-let me go!" she gasped when his punishment finally ended. "I'm not the suicidal type, and well you know it, but if you don't stop hurting me I might begin to wish I *had* killed myself!"

Scott's face was a white mask of fury that frightened her even more than the punishment he had dished out as he dragged her against his hard chest and, for one heart-stopping moment, she thought he was going to kiss her, but he thrust her from him violently and practically dragged her to where she had left her robe and sandals. He helped her into her robe with hands that seemed to have lost the art of gentleness, and waited for her to slip her feet into her sandals before he gripped her arm and marched her up to the house as if she were an erring child. Anna's legs were shaking like jelly when they climbed the steps up on to the terrace, but his hand on her arm was a sweet yet agonising support she was secretly thankful for.

"I suggest you don't mention this incident to Aunt Dorrie," he instructed her coldly when he released her at the entrance. "And I would exercise a little more care in future, if I were you."

Anna's glance flickered over him nervously, taking in the broadness of his tanned shoulders, and the slim hips clad in blue swimming trunks. She was reminded, with inevitable nostalgia, of that afternoon he had come walking across the sand towards her. Lighthearted bantering had eventually led to her being thrown into the sea with her clothes on, and as the memory of those happy moments flashed through her mind, she choked back a sob and brushed past him through the door. She did not stop until she had reached her room, and only then did she release the tears she had found so difficult to keep in check from the moment he had scooped her out of the ocean.

It had been a dreadful experience coming so close to death, she recalled as she showered and washed the sand out of her hair, and her legs threatened to cave in beneath her when she thought of what might have happened if Scott had not arrived at that precise moment.

At dinner that evening she had the strangest sensation that Scott was observing her, but she found him concentrating on his food whenever she looked up. It was only when he excused himself from the table that he actually met her glance and, for one brief moment, a flicker of emotion flashed across his harsh face before he left the dining-room to closet himself in his study for the evening.

Aunt Dorrie retired to her room almost immediately after dinner, but Anna found herself pacing the living-room floor restlessly. The frightening incident in the sea that afternoon had made her temporarily forget her encounter with Joan Mulder earlier that day, and Anna wondered nervously just how and when Joan would act upon the threats she had made.

Strangely enough, she did not have long to wait in order to find out, for the telephone rang in the hall just as Anna passed it and, lifting the receiver, she found herself recognising Joan's melodious voice immediately.

"I would like to speak to Scott, please," Joan demanded without preamble.

Anna was still contemplating an acceptable excuse when Scott's voice came calmly and clearly over the line. "Thank you, Anna, I'll take the call on the extension here in the study."

"Scott!" Joan breathed the words with a husky sensuality in her voice. "How wonderful to have found you in!"

Anna replaced the receiver hurriedly as if it had stung her, but she found she was shaking uncontrollably while Joan's "Scott!" kept ringing in her ears. She would not dare to listen in, but she would give almost anything to know what they were talking about at that moment. Relinquishing her intention to retire early, she remained in the living-room and waited while the anxious minutes passed with agonising slowness. Surely Scott would explain the reason for Joan's call? But then, why should he! What she and Scott had to say to each other was really none of her business, unless, of course, it affected her directly, Anna decided uncomfortably, and it most certainly *would* affect her if Joan carried out the threats she had made that morning.

The telephone in the hall clicked, indicating that the call had ended, and Anna froze where she stood beside the window when she heard the study door open. Scott was going to explain to her after all, her heart rejoiced wildly, but when he stood framed in the living-room door she knew, without doubt, that an explanation was the last thing he had in mind at that moment.

"I'm going out for a while, Anna, and I have no idea what time I shall be back," he announced, searching his jacket pocket absently to make sure that he had his keys, and Anna stood there as if she had been turned to stone.

Scott was going out to meet Joan – the realisation flashed across her tortured mind as if it had been written there in glaring neon lights, and there was a sick feeling at the pit of her stomach as she watched him leave the house. His instant reaction to Joan's call indicated only one thing to Anna at that moment. He still cared for her!

She heard the Mercedes being driven down the driveway, and jealousy stabbed at her like heated knives. Was it possible that Scott had felt like this when he had waited in the garden of her parents' home that night only to find that she had been alone with Andrew? she wondered crazily. Could his reaction have been prompted by jealousy?

It was a tantalising thought, but she discarded it almost at once. Jealousy was the sometimes destructive emotion which usually accompanied love, and Scott did not love her, for he had never once said so. If Scott loved her, he would surely have shelved his pride long ago, and would have been eager to give her the opportunity to explain away the unpleasant suspicions which had arisen as a result of that unfortunate incident?

Anna's temples began to throb painfully, and she felt indescribably weary as she went up to her room. It would be useless waiting around in the living-room in the hope that Scott would explain when he returned home, and his mood lately was not the kind that encouraged questioning.

She took a couple of tablets to ease her headache and went to bed, but sleep eluded her. Was Scott allowing Joan to ensnare him a second time? Were they planning, perhaps, how to extricate themselves from the ties which bound them in order to be together again?

'Oh, God, don't let this happen,' she thought, groaning inwardly. 'What am I going to do if he asks for his freedom?'

During the next two days, prior to the Mayor's Ball, Scott made no attempt to offer an explanation for Joan's call, and the tension between them increased to a point where Anna began to feel as though everything within her had become suspended – waiting and hoping for something, *anything* which would bring relief from this unbearable situation.

On the day of the Ball Anna walked along the beach-front, and the brightly coloured umbrellas of the bathers, against the backdrop of the blue sky and shimmering blue sea, lent an inexplicable air of festivity to a day which as usual had started drearily for her. The summer holidays would soon begin, she realised absently, and

Amazibu Bay would become crowded with tourists from all parts of the country, just like every other holiday resort along the Natal coast. Whether the rush of tourists would affect Scott at all, she had no idea, but if it meant that he would be away from home more often than usual, she could only hope that they would have reached some sort of understanding by then to compensate for the periods when they would be separated.

The heat was stifling and Anna's body felt clammy beneath the cool cotton frock when she joined Scott's aunt on the shady terrace for a cool and refreshing lemon drink after her walk along the beach-front.

"Scott telephoned while you were out," Aunt Dorrie told her. "He won't be home until this evening."

"Did he say where he was going?" Anna asked a little anxiously.

"I think he said he had some business to attend to in Durban," Aunt Dorrie replied thoughtfully, taking a sip of her drink before she added smilingly, "He said we weren't to worry. He expected to be home early enough to be at the Ball this evening."

A nasty suspicion reared its ugly head in Anna's mind. Was Scott's sudden trip to Durban really connected with business? Anna tried to shake off these distasteful thoughts, but they lingered in her subconscious like a nagging headache for which there was no remedy.

CHAPTER NINE

ANNA quivered with nervous anticipation while she dressed for the Ball that evening, and she took more care than usual with her appearance. The amber-coloured gown had been styled to expose the creamy smoothness of her shoulders, while it cleverly accentuated the gentle curve of her breasts and the rounded fullness of her hips. Her hair had been pinned up on to her head, and the emerald necklace, which had been a gift from Scott before their marriage, matched the colour of her eyes to perfection.

Her hands trembled a little as she smoothed away an imaginary crease in the full-length skirt, and she paused a moment longer in front of the mirror to inspect herself critically. It was important that she looked her best that night if her plans were to succeed at all. She was determined to penetrate the barrier Scott had placed between them, and if she succeeded in re-awakening just a spark of interest, then her efforts would not have been futile.

Glancing at the time on the bedside clock, she realised she could not keep Scott waiting very much longer and, picking up her silk wrap and evening purse, she went down to join him. She paused momentarily in the hall, however, suddenly not so sure that she was capable of carrying out this little game which smacked faintly of seduction, but she rebuked herself for her faintheartedness and pulled herself together seconds before she entered the living-room.

Her heart behaved like a wild thing in her breast when

she saw Scott standing with his back to her at the open window, and her hungry glance lingered on his tall, immaculate figure in the perfectly tailored evening suit. The breadth of his shoulders seemed to be accentuated by the black jacket, and his dark hair glistened in the light as if it was still damp from his shower.

He turned then, as if sensing her presence, and their eyes met and held for a few heart-stopping seconds. Anna hardly dared to breathe for fear of breaking the spell which seemed to have taken them back in time, and which had somehow replaced the fires in his devastating blue glance as it swept over her with the intimacy and warmth of a caress.

The glass in his hand seemed to shake a little, she noticed with satisfaction, and he swallowed down its contents hastily before approaching her.

"You're looking exceedingly beautiful this evening, Anna," he remarked with a casualness that did not match the look in his eyes.

Anna smiled, rising to the occasion. "A compliment from you, Scott, has become something quite rare lately, but . . . thank you."

"There was a time when you would have accused me of flattery," he reminded her with a wry, faintly cynical smile.

"Perhaps I'm in need of a little confidence this evening."

"Confidence?" he echoed a little incredulously. "I've always thought you possessed plenty of confidence and self-reliance."

He would not have said that had he been aware of how her insides were quivering at that moment, she thought with a touch of humour. "I think there comes a time in everyone's life when a little added confidence could make all the difference in the world."

"And you're in need of that extra bit of confidence this evening?" he questioned curiously, his glance sliding over her smooth shoulders and lingering deliberately where the bodice of her gown plunged a fraction to reveal the enticing cleavage between her breasts.

"Yes, I am," she admitted a little breathlessly as she avoided the disturbing intensity of his eyes.

"Why?"

"I wish I knew the reason myself," she replied softly after a reflective pause as to why she should be nervous of the man she loved. He was suddenly so close to her that she was able to catch a whiff of the familiar odour of his after-shave lotion, and she glanced anxiously at the bronze, ornately carved clock above the mantelshelf. "Isn't it about time we left?"

"Yes, it is," he agreed quietly, and his hand beneath her elbow sent a current of exciting awareness along her receptive nerves.

The large hall at the Tom-Tom, used exclusively for entertainment purposes, was decorated with festive lights for this annual occasion. The doors leading out on to the terrace were flung wide, and the band had begun to entice the specially invited guests on to the floor when Scott parked the car in the space allotted to him.

Anna found, to her dismay, that they were to join the Mayor and his wife at the main table with some others. There was a quick reshuffling at their approach, and Anna was seated with Mayor Collins on her left, while Scott sat further to her left beside the grey-haired, elegantly dressed Mrs. Collins.

Anna's initial nervousness soon evaporated when she discovered that the Mayor was actually a very nice old gentleman. He had an amusing habit of wriggling his large, greying moustache, and Anna had to forcibly suppress a giggle on several occasions. Her wary glance, however, continually searched for some sign of Joan Mulder, and she hoped, rather ungenerously, that something would happen to keep the other woman away.

Scott was obliged to dance the first dance with Mrs. Collins, while Anna was jogged about in a jolly fashion by Mayor Collins, then they changed partners, and Anna found herself in Scott's arms at last. As if by request, the band played a melody with a slow, rhythmic throb, and Scott's arm tightened about Anna's waist until their bodies touched.

The moment Anna had waited for all day had arrived, and she relaxed against him, every nerve in her body responding to his nearness in the most exciting way. It seemed to her as though a century had passed since the last time he had held her in his arms, but despite this she matched her steps faultlessly to his. His warm breath fanned her forehead, and her pulse quickened when, a moment later, she heard him groan softly and lower his head until his lips touched her ear.

"You're so beautiful, Anna," he said, the deep timbre of his voice sending a shiver of half-forgotten delight through her. "You're so beautiful you'd go to any man's head."

"Do I go to yours, Scott?" she whispered in a daringly provocative voice.

"Do I need to answer that?" he groaned again, demonstrating only too clearly, in the way he held her against him, that she had succeeded in awakening a flame of desire in him.

"No, you don't need to answer that," she murmured in reply and, lowering her head on to his shoulder, gave herself up to the magic of the moment.

His reaction to her nearness had given her hope for the future, and for a few blissful minutes no one else existed except Scott and herself. The music ended all too soon, however, and Scott led her back to the table, but not before she had felt his lips brush warmly against the side of her mouth. Had his slight kiss been accidental, or deliberate? she wondered dreamily, deciding on the latter in preference to the other.

Her tentative hopes for the evening were rudely shattered before they could reach their table, for Joan Mulder stepped into their path and severed the newly established link by her mere presence. Her shimmering black gown clung to her curvaceous body, revealing far more than it concealed, and Anna felt her own cheeks grow hot with embarrassment for Joan's sake.

"Darling, I'm so sorry I'm late. I had one of those dreadful migraines again," she purred up at Scott as if he had issued her with a personal invitation to attend the Ball. "Do you remember how you used to sit beside my bed and bathe my forehead with iced water until the pain eased?"

Her deliberate reference to the past was as objectionable as it was infuriating, but Scott seemed to take the remark in his stride.

"I remember doing so once, yes," he said calmly with a faintly censorious smile hovering about his mouth.

"I could have done with your ministrations today, darling," she continued, smiling up at Scott enticingly as she raised her hand and stroked his cheek with a possessive familiarity that made Anna choke back her rising fury. Then, ignoring Anna's rigid presence beside Scott, she asked: "Shall we dance?"

Anna expected Scott to make some sort of excuse, judging by his now impassive features, but he inclined his head slightly and, without so much as a glance in Anna's direction, he escorted Joan on to the floor.

The evening became a nightmare when Joan pulled up a chair and sat down quite brazenly beside Scott. She monopolised him almost the entire evening, and although he danced with other women occasionally, Anna could not help noticing that he somehow danced mostly with Joan. Anna never lacked partners either but, whether by accident or design, she did not dance with Scott again.

Jealousy and pain were her constant companions for the evening, and an incredible anger simmered just below the surface of her conscious mind when she saw how closely, and intimately Scott and Joan were dancing together. How *dare* he do this to me! she kept thinking, and when she recalled how close she had been to him during that first dance, she could have wept with despair.

She was humiliatingly aware of the way people were glancing at her and whispering behind her back. She could not blame them, for they certainly had reason, but she had never imagined, not even in her wildest dreams, that Scott would ever treat her in this way. Could he not see what was happening? Did he not realise that the way he smiled and flirted with Joan was attracting the attention of everyone at the Ball, and subjecting her to the worst kind of humiliation she had ever had to endure?

Anna slowly unclenched her hands as she stared at Scott, and she was surprised to find that her palms were wet with perspiration. The evening which she had planned with such care had turned into a fiasco. She had been filled with hope at the prospect of going to the Ball, but now her plans were almost laughable, if it were not so painful. Her husband had spent almost the entire evening dancing with his ex-girl-friend, holding her as if he could not bear to let her go, and allowing her to come very close to making love to him in public. It was disgusting, degrading ... and so terribly, *terribly* humiliating!

Mayor Collins and his wife returned to the table and Anna blinked back the suggestion of tears in her eyes. It would not do to be seen weeping in public, she told herself firmly as she forced her stiff, unwilling lips into the smile she had been forced to wear all evening.

It was virtually impossible to converse normally, and naturally, with these two elderly people beside her, who must have noticed that something was dreadfully wrong, but tactfully refrained from remarking upon it. They were a nice, friendly couple, but Anna found her attention suddenly elsewhere instead of with what they were saying.

The music had not ended, but Joan appeared at their table to collect her things and, without so much as a polite word to the Mayor and his wife, she marched out of the hall by way of the side entrance. It was not quite midnight, Anna noticed absently, and then a wave of cynicism swept through her. Was Joan leaving the Ball in true Cinderella fashion after her overwhelming success with Scott?

"Shall we dance?" a deep voice asked beside her and, as she looked up to find Scott smiling down at her, she felt herself begin to shake with an anger so violent that it almost blinded her temporarily.

How *dare* he think that she would be only too willing to fall back into his waiting arms now that Joan was no longer there for him to amuse himself with! How *dare* he humiliate her all evening, and then behave as though nothing out of the ordinary had happened!

Stifling her anger forcibly, she said in a voice that sounded quite unlike her own, "I think I would prefer to go home now, if you don't mind."

Scott's smile faded as her stormy glance met his and, without a word, he waited for her to collect her wrap and purse. They said goodnight to Mayor Collins and his wife and then, as several pairs of eyes observed them unashamedly, Anna raised her head proudly and walked stiffly and erectly from the hall with Scott at her side.

The atmosphere in the car was deadly, and neither of them made any attempt to speak. Anna fumed silently, giving free rein to her thoughts. And Scott ... ? What did it matter to her what Scott thought! He must be fully aware of what he had done, and if his conscience – if he had a conscience at all – was keeping him silent, then she hoped he squirmed inwardly with remorse.

They parted company in stony silence outside her bedroom door, and Anna wasted no time in changing out of her expensive evening gown, the violence of her movements reflecting her emotions when she eventually tightened the belt of her dressing gown about her waist, creamed off her make-up, and removed the pins from her hair to let it fall in a soft, red-gold disarray about her shoulders.

Never in her life had she been so furious before, or so humiliated. 'Or so jealous,' a little voice added for her. She lowered her brush and stared directly into her angry eyes reflected in the mirror.

'Yes, I *am* jealous,' she admitted to herself. 'I'm jealous of someone else receiving what I crave so desperately, and can't have. I want his love, and without that I might as well have nothing.'

A light tap on her door made her tense instantly, and her back went rigid with antagonism when Scott entered the room and closed the door softly behind him. He had showered and changed into a soft white towelling robe that accentuated his tanned, muscular fitness to perfection, she noticed absently, but at that moment she was blind to his physical appeal; blind to the sensuality of that mouth which could create such havoc with her emotions; and blind to the strange hesitancy in his manner as he approached her.

The only thing she could see at that moment was the way he had held Joan when he had danced with her, and the way he had smiled when he had looked down into her eyes. Joan's body had been arched sensually towards his at one stage, and he had made no visible effort to discourage her blatant advances.

"Anna ..." Scott began, reaching for her, but she was on her feet and moving a pace away from him almost in the same instant.

"Don't touch me!" she said through clenched teeth as she fought against the pain inflicted upon her by the visions flashing across her mind.

"What is this?" he demanded, recovering swiftly from his astonishment. "You didn't appear to find my touch objectionable when we danced together this evening, and I could have sworn you welcomed it. What's changed your mind?"

That he should have the audacity to ask her that, was beyond any stretch of her imagination, and her fury erupted with a violence that shook through her like a tornado.

"That's just it!" she spat out the words. "You danced with me once, and for a moment during that dance I thought it possible for us to bridge the widening gap between us, but then Joan arrived, and for the rest of the evening I had to watch you dancing and flirting with her in the most outrageous manner!"

Scott's face darkened. "I object to that remark."

"And I object to the way you treated me this evening," she countered swiftly. "You humiliated me in every possible way by clinging to Joan as though you couldn't let her go, and deliberately ignoring my existence the rest of the time."

"I didn't notice that you exactly lacked partners," he hit back at her relentlessly.

"What did you expect me to do?" she demanded sarcastically. "Sit at the table like a good little girl, and refuse every man who came my way in the hope that my husband might eventually condescend to ask me for a dance?"

"Don't be ridiculous, Anna!"

"So now I'm being ridiculous, am I?" she almost shouted, her eyes unusually beautiful at that moment as they flashed green sparks of anger at him. "After the way Joan pitched up uninvited here at the house, baldly stating that she intended to break up our marriage, you surely didn't expect me to take the entire incident calmly, did you?"

A brief smile curved his lips, but it was gone almost before it had appeared. "I believe you handled the situation admirably."

Anna sucked her breath in sharply. Only his aunt could have told him of that encounter with Joan, and knowing now that he had been aware of it only served to increase her anger.

"What do you suppose people were thinking when they saw you and Joan together this evening?" she demanded scathingly. "And what an exciting bit of scandal you created by ignoring me while you danced with your old girl-friend more often than was necessary, and held her far too close to dispel the speculations of every interested party."

"I don't want to argue with you, Anna," he said tiredly. "I'm flying to Lesotho tomorrow on business, and I won't be back until Sunday evening at the earliest."

"How nice!" she exclaimed in a voice that was heavy with sarcasm. "Are you taking Joan along for the ride?"

"Be sensible, Anna," he instructed her with infuriating calmness. "I'm in the throes of buying that hotel in Lesotho I told you about once, and I'll hardly have time for the kind of frivolity you have in mind."

"How do I know what you'll have time for?" she insisted, clamping down firmly on her rising hysteria as she thought of how differently she had planned the ending to that evening. "You were seldom home this past week, you hardly spoke to me unless you absolutely had to, and I've been forced to spend my nights in solitary splendour in that enormous bed," she ended her tirade in a voice that shook noticeably.

"Anna, don't be this way," he pleaded suddenly, holding out his arms towards her invitingly, but she stepped back jerkily as if she had been stung by a viper.

"Leave me alone!" she cried hoarsely, horrifyingly close to tears. "I couldn't bear you to touch me!"

"You don't mean that," he rasped, white about the mouth.

"I *do* mean it!" she insisted adamantly, her body shaking so much that she had to clutch at the wardrobe to steady herself. "I'm tired of being made a fool of, and I won't be humiliated by you again, so leave me alone!"

Scott's features were taut with some kind of inner emotion she was too distraught to analyse as he said thickly, "I never intended to humiliate you, or to make a fool of you, Anna."

"Whatever your intentions were, they don't interest me at the moment," she replied, and her voice was cold and detached with the effort to control herself. "All I want at the moment is to be left alone in peace."

The silence in the room was charged with conflicting emotions as they stood facing each other, and between them lay a chasm so wide that nothing short of a miracle would ever help them bridge it.

"Well, if that's the way you want it, then I suppose there's nothing I can do about it," he said quietly, his expression shuttered.

"That's the way I want it," she insisted in a voice that sounded flat and lifeless to her own ears.

Her statement seemed to hang suspended in the air between them like the blade of the guillotine, and it fell with a painful precision as the door closed behind Scott, awakening her to the finality of her actions.

"What have I done!" she groaned, burying her ashen face in her trembling hands. "What have I done!"

It all seemed so worthless now. Her jealousy, her anger, and her humiliation all seemed so negligible now in the face of her suffering if Scott should leave her, and God knows she had just gone out of her way to encourage him to do what she feared most.

She sat down heavily on the edge of the bed as her legs gave way beneath her, and she felt curiously tired now that the storm of fury inside her had spent itself. She toyed frantically with the idea of going to Scott, but what could she say? How could she explain?

She tried to find an explanation for his outrageous behaviour at the Ball, and failed. How could he have led her to believe that there was reason to hope for a reconciliation, only to ignore her the rest of the evening by dancing attendance on Joan?

Anna climbed into bed wearily and switched off the light, but she tossed about restlessly as the evening's events flashed through her tortured mind. She could almost feel Scott's arms about her as they had been at the start of the evening, and hear his voice as he said: "You're so beautiful, Anna, you would go to any man's head." Was that perhaps the crux of it all? She had gone to his head, but she had never really succeeded in reaching his heart?

She turned over once again and plumped up her pillows. Could it be true? *Could it?* Did Scott love Joan?

"Oh, no, no, it can't be true? It *mustn't* be true!" Anna moaned softly and urgently into the darkness, turning her face into the pillows as if it would help to shut out the thought, but it persisted relentlessly until she was forced to admit that it was the only logical explanation she could find for Scott's behaviour.

He had not intended to humiliate her, he had said, and if this was so, then what had he meant to convey to her by his actions? Had that perhaps been his way of making it clear to her that he wanted out of their marriage?

An incredibly heavy weight seemed to lodge itself in Anna's chest all at once, and her breathing became inexplicably laboured. If Scott loved Joan, then there was nothing Anna could do to hold him, and it would be just as Joan had predicted.

"Goodbye, Anna."

Startled, she sat up in bed, her breath rasping in her throat. Scott's voice had come to her so clearly that she could almost have sworn that he had said those words himself, instead of them merely being reproduced in her mind.

Was it going to be 'Goodbye, Anna,' again?

First it had been Andrew, and now it was Scott. It had taken her several soul-searching months to recover from the illusion that she had loved and lost Andrew. How was she going to recover from this very real love she had for Scott?

The sound of the surf came wafting into her room, carried by the breeze through her open window, and she wished suddenly that Scott had left her to drown when she had found herself caught in the current and relentlessly dragged out to sea. Death would have been preferable compared to living a life without Scott.

Anna choked on a sob and tried to check the hot tears that flowed so freely down her cheeks, but she gave up the uneven struggle and wept until she lay exhausted against the tear-dampened pillows to drift into a fitful sleep.

CHAPTER TEN

The shadows beneath Anna's eyes were there as evidence of her restless night and, with nothing but hours of inactivity ahead of her, she found herself incapable of doing justice to the plate of bacon and eggs which had been placed before her.

"You're not eating your breakfast, child," Aunt Dorrie finally remarked, her glance concerned when she noticed that Anna was merely rearranging the contents of her plate.

Putting down her knife and fork, Anna pushed her plate aside with a grimace and settled for a cup of strong black coffee. "I'm not very hungry."

Aunt Dorrie refrained from comment, but her shrewd glance observed the faint tremor in the hands that raised the cup to Anna's lips. "I saw Scott leaving the house early this morning."

"He's flying to Lesotho for the weekend on business," Anna said quietly.

"Oh, dear!" Aunt Dorrie's fork paused on its way to her mouth. "That means you'll be left alone here for the weekend if I visit my friends down at Port Shepstone as planned."

"That doesn't matter."

"You could come with me, of course," she offered hastily. "The Fergusons would love to have you, and there's plenty of room in their cottage."

Anna lowered her cup and shook her head firmly. "I would rather stay, if you don't mind. I'm sure there's plenty to do, and I won't mind being on my own at all."

"Are you sure, Anna?" the older woman asked with concern. "I could very easily give the Fergusons a ring and arrange to see them some other time."

"No!" Anna said hastily. She had to come to some sort of decision about the future, and she preferred the idea of being alone. "Don't do that, Aunt Dorrie. Please don't alter your arrangements for my sake."

There was a lengthy silence while Dorothy MacPherson finished her breakfast and poured herself a cup of coffee, then she sat back and regarded Anna closely. "What's the matter, my dear? You look as though you didn't get much sleep last night. Are you ill?"

"No – no, I'm not ill at all," Anna stammered foolishly, looking away.

"Is it something to do with Scott?"

"No, it isn't," Anna lied hastily.

Aunt Dorrie's lips tightened as she leaned towards Anna. "If you're not ill, and it's nothing to do with Scott, then would you mind telling me why you're crying?"

Startled, Anna raised her hands to her cheeks and

found, to her dismay, that they were damp.

"I'm just being silly, I suppose," she laughed a little shakily, but the laugh ended on a choked sob and, getting to her feet hastily, she walked across to the window to stare out at the grey, dismal-looking sky.

It was going to rain, she thought, trying to keep her mind fixed on something as mundane as the weather while she tried to get a grip on herself, but Aunt Dorrie was apparently not going to leave the matter there.

"I'm not a fool, my dear," Anna heard her say calmly. "Things haven't been as they should be between you and Scott this past week. The atmosphere has been so thick at times I could have cut it with a knife." She pushed her chair back and came to Anna's side. "Don't think me an interfering old woman, my dear, but it sometimes helps to talk to someone about the things that trouble you."

Anna hesitated. It had never been easy for her to confide in anyone, but she could not deny that she had a need to talk to someone; someone who could perhaps make some sense out of the entire situation. She turned to meet the warm, sympathetic glance of the woman she had come to care for, but still she hesitated. "I shouldn't really burden you with my problems, Aunt Dorrie."

"Nonsense, child," Aunt Dorrie smiled encouragingly as she led Anna back to the table and poured them each a fresh cup of coffee. "Now tell me all about it."

Anna swallowed down a mouthful of coffee to boost her courage, and finally relented. "It began when Scott came to see me in Johannesburg while my father was so ill."

"I thought so," Aunt Dorrie remarked suddenly. "He arrived home looking like a thundercloud about to erupt at any moment, but go on."

Anna explained briefly about the relationship which

had once existed between Andrew and herself, about her meeting with Andrew because of the problems which had arisen between Debbie and himself, and of how Scott had witnessed her arrival at her parents' house in the company of Andrew.

"I can quite imagine what Scott must have thought," Anna said unsteadily, "but he's refused to listen to any explanation, and because of this everything has somehow gone from bad to worse."

"Is that all?" Aunt Dorrie prompted gently when Anna fell silent.

"No," she shook her head and sighed unhappily. "You overheard the conversation I had with Joan, but I don't think you know that she telephoned Scott that same evening. They spoke for some time, and then he left the house directly afterwards, presumably to pay her a visit."

"Did he actually say he was going to see her?"

"No, but where else would he have gone immediately after speaking to her on the phone, and then ..." She hesitated, pressing her fingers against her aching eyes. "... and then there was the fiasco at the Ball last night."

"I gather Joan was there?" Aunt Dorrie guessed shrewdly.

"Yes." Anna took another mouthful of coffee when she felt her insides begin to shake. "I've never been so humiliated in all my life."

"Did she try to cause trouble?"

"I have no doubt that she was aiming at that, but it was the way Scott behaved that hurt most," Anna admitted in a choked voice, cringing inwardly as every painful detail flashed across her mind. "He encouraged her quite openly until people began to talk about the way he ignored me to dance mostly with her, and I'm afraid Scott and I had a flaming row when we arrived home last night."

"Is it the fact that you had a row that is upsetting you so much?" the older woman asked gently.

"Not entirely, no." Anna bit down hard on a trembling lip. "I have given the matter a great deal of thought, Aunt Dorrie, and I think Joan was right. Scott *does* care for her."

"That's impossible!" Aunt Dorrie said sharply, shaking her head and frowning. "It was all over a long time ago. She tried her best to get him after Trudie died, and failed."

Anna smiled a little wanly. "Love isn't something one can switch on and off at will, Aunt Dorrie, and it isn't always sensible either. When you love someone, you love them despite all their faults, and he ... Scott did feel something for Joan once."

"She imagined that he did," Aunt Dorrie insisted stubbornly. "He never loved her the way he loves you."

Anna looked away hastily and blinked back the tears which had gathered in her eyes. "Scott has never once said he loves me."

"But he *does* love you."

"You wouldn't say that if you saw him with Joan last night," Anna replied disconsolately, staring out of the window and noticing the fine spray of rain against the panes.

"You don't think that he was perhaps trying to make you jealous?" Aunt Dorrie suggested at length.

"No," Anna sighed, pushing her empty cup aside and interlacing her fingers so tightly that they ached. "One dance with her would have succeeded in making me jealous, and it did, but several dances went a little beyond such a desire, I think."

"Did Scott offer you any explanation for his behaviour?"

"I'm afraid that I didn't really give him much of an opportunity to do so," Anna confessed ruefully. "I was so furious that I lashed out at him blindly, and said many things which I regret now."

Aunt Dorrie's expression was thoughtful and troubled as she stared at Anna. "I really don't know what to say to you, except that I'm sure you're wrong about him and Joan."

"I hope so too, but –" Her throat tightened, choking back the words as she rose to her feet and walked restlessly across to the window once more to stare out into the garden. Her vision blurred suddenly, and whether it was as a result of the raindrops against the window-pane, or the tears in her eyes, she could not say at that moment as she voiced her decision. "I think I should go away for a while. Perhaps for just a few days. It would give Scott the opportunity to decide about the future without my presence to complicate matters."

"You mean you would give him to Joan without putting up a fight?" Aunt Dorrie asked incredulously.

"If that's what he really wants, and if it would make him happy, then I shan't stand in his way."

"You love him that much?" Aunt Dorrie asked softly after a brief, enlightening pause.

Anna's lips trembled, but she managed to control herself and whispered, "Yes."

"You're a remarkable young woman, Anna," Aunt Dorrie said at length, coming to Anna's side and touching her arm lightly. "Not many women would sit back and allow their husbands to be taken from them because they think they might be happy with someone else."

"What would be the use of holding on to Scott if, in his heart, he wants Joan?" Anna demanded chokingly, her despair clearly visible in the dark green depths of her beautiful eyes as she turned to the woman beside her. "I don't think I could bear to live with him while knowing that he loves someone else."

"Anna, don't leave just yet," Aunt Dorrie pleaded, her hand tightening on Anna's arm. "Think very carefully before you do something you may regret for the rest of your life."

"But it's all so hopeless, Aunt Dorrie," Anna cried, burying her quivering face in her hands in an effort to fight back the tears.

"It may seem hopeless to you now, but some things need time to resolve themselves," the older woman advised, placing a motherly arm about Anna's shoulders. "Don't give up, my dear. I'm sure that somewhere there must be a reasonable explanation for all that's happened."

"Oh, I don't know what to think any more. I'm so confused."

"Promise me you'll at least stay until Scott returns from this business trip," Aunt Dorrie insisted persuasively.

"I promise," Anna whispered after a moment, lowering her hands to continue staring dully through the window.

"You don't want to change your mind and come with me?"

"No." Anna shook her head and took a deep breath to control herself before she was able to face the slender, grey-haired woman beside her. "You go and have a lovely weekend, Aunt Dorrie, and thank you for listening to me."

Aunt Dorrie's blue eyes clouded. "I only wish I was capable of helping you in some way."

"It has helped tremendously just being able to talk about it," Anna assured her hastily, kissing her spontaneously on her soft cheek. "Don't let me keep you any longer."

"Take care of yourself, my dear," Aunt Dorrie smiled briefly and encouragingly before she went upstairs to collect her overnight bag.

When Dorothy MacPherson's small Austin disappeared down the drive a few minutes later, Anna turned away from the window with a quivering sigh. It was going to be a long weekend on her own with nothing but her thoughts for company, but her mind was in such a turmoil that she would have been a very undesirable companion in her present state, she decided as she left the breakfast-room and allowed the servants to clear the table.

Anna sifted listlessly through the mail when it was delivered later that morning, but a worried frown creased her brow when she came across an envelope addressed to her in a familiar handwriting. It was from Andrew, she realised instantly and, leaving the rest of the mail on the hall table, she went into the living-room and stared undecidedly at the envelope for a few seconds before she sat down and opened it.

"Dear Anna," it began in that irregular, sometimes illegible handwriting, "I never had the opportunity to speak to you privately before you left, but I would like to say thank you for giving Debbie and me your shoulder to cry on.

"We had a lengthy discussion, Debbie and I, and I felt it was only right that I should tell her of our meeting that Friday evening, and the reason for it. I wouldn't want it to come out at a later date to cast an unnecessary shadow on our marriage. Debbie understands and, knowing that you have found the happiness you so richly deserve with your husband has made all the difference to us. We both realise now that we had foolishly allowed our guilt to spoil things for us. We should have discussed it, instead of hiding it from each other, but you, dear sensible Anna, made it possible for us to overcome our problems, and to learn from our mistakes.

"I don't know how we shall ever be able to thank you enough, but Debbie and I wish you everything you could possibly wish for yourself in the future. Regards, Andrew."

Anna lowered the letter and stared dismally at the shaggy-haired carpet beneath her sandalled feet. Debbie and Andrew had at last managed to sort out their difficulties, but that was more than she could say for Scott and herself. "Dear sensible Anna," Andrew had written, but she was not so certain that she was being very sensible in the handling of her own affairs. Was she not being a fool to remain as Aunt Dorrie had made her promise to do? What purpose would it serve to prolong the inevitable, and to cling to Scott when he no longer wanted her?

She folded Andrew's letter and pushed it into the pocket of her skirt, forcing herself not to dwell on her unhappy thoughts. The rainy weather kept her indoors all morning and, after trying to eat a light lunch, she switched on the radio and picked up a magazine. The music soothed her considerably while she paged idly through the magazine, but the programme was interrupted a few minutes later for the hourly news bulletin. Rising irritably, she stepped across the carpeted floor, but her fingers never touched the dial on the radio as the smooth voice of the news reader suddenly captured her horrified attention with an item of news that succeeded in draining every vestige of colour from her face.

"The light aircraft chartered by Mr. Scott Beresford, wealthy hotelier, has been reported missing on a flight to Lesotho. It is said that radio contact was lost shortly after the aircraft struck bad weather conditions on approaching the Drakensberg, and airport officials have been alerted in that area. Two other men are accompanying Mr. Beresford on this flight, his lawyer, Mr. Joshua Gray, and his accountant, Mr. . . ."

Anna switched off the radio with a jerky movement, but she was hardly aware of what she was doing. Fear such as she had never known before clutched at her heart and chilled the blood in her veins, and she sank into the nearest chair as her legs caved in beneath her. Everything within her seemed to have ceased functioning, except for the loud drumming in her ears, and the wild, horrifying thoughts which had become manifested in her chaotic mind. Scott's aircraft had been reported missing, and God only knows whether he was still alive!

She groaned in anguish, burying her ashen face in her trembling hands as she tried to shut out the frightening possibility that she might never see him again. If anything happened to Scott, she would never forgive herself for the things she had said, and the way she had sent him away from her the night before, she thought wildly.

"Pull yourself together, Anna!" she told herself fiercely at last as she fought against the desire to weep hysterically. "Nothing was said in the news bulletin about Scott and the other passengers being killed, and until there's news of that nature, there's reason to hope that they're still alive and possibly grounded somewhere for a very good reason."

Her hysteria subsided gradually, but no amount of reasoning could diminish her fears and, realising that she would go mad if she did not do something, she got shakily to her feet and went into the hall. A telephone call to the airport authorities in Durban offered her no comfort at all. There was no further information regarding the disappearance of the aircraft chartered by Scott, but she at least had the satisfaction of knowing that they would telephone her the moment there was anything to report.

Anna could not sit down again after that, and neither was she allowed to. The telephone rang incessantly, and she was inundated with calls from people they knew, and others she had never heard of before. Sheila and Morris telephoned from Durban, and Aunt Dorrie from Port Shepstone. Anna replied to their frantic queries to the best of her ability, forcing herself to sound reassuring, but there seemed to be absolutely no way of reassuring herself as her fear increased with every passing second.

She paced the floor relentlessly when the telephone calls finally ceased, and the silence in the house enfolded her like a blanket of oppression. Her anxiety became a living thing that tortured her with visions of Scott's strong, virile body lying battered and crushed in the wreckage of the aircraft, and she wrapped her arms about herself as if to ward off her thoughts physically, and the agonising pain that accompanied them.

It seemed to her as if several hours had passed since she had first heard the dreadful news of Scott's aircraft being reported missing, but the clock on the mantelshelf indicated that it was less than an hour ago. Anna hovered beside the telephone, contemplating whether she should telephone the authorities again, but she decided against it and resumed her restless pacing of the living-room floor. They had said they would let her know the moment they received any news, but this period of waiting was becoming increasingly difficult to endure.

If only it would stop raining, she thought as she caught her knuckles between her teeth and bit down hard while she paced up and down. She was being ridiculous, she supposed, but if she sat down now she would burst into tears, and tears would solve nothing at the moment.

"Oh, Scott, Scott!" she prayed in her heart. "Wherever you are, come back to me. *Please* come back to me!"

"Goodbye, Anna," Scott's voice taunted her, and she drew a shuddering breath as she buried her face in her cold, shaking hands.

"Oh, God," she thought frantically, fear circulating through her body like a paralysing numbness that made her subside weakly into a chair. "Don't let it be goodbye. Not like this!"

Anna stared blindly into space, seeing nothing and hearing nothing until she was brought to her senses by the sound of footsteps on the carpeted floor of the hall. She was on her feet at once, wondering who it could be, but when her visitor stepped into the room she felt certain that she was suffering from hallucinations. The living-room tilted crazily about her, and she clutched at the chair beside her for support, her eyes wide and dark in her pale, ravaged face. She passed a shaky hand over her eyes, half afraid her hallucination would disappear, but it remained standing in the doorway. She wondered for a moment whether she was going mad, but when that faintly mocking smile touched his lips, she could no longer restrain herself.

"Scott!" His name was wrenched hoarsely from her lips as her feet carried her across the room towards him and, not caring what he must think of her, she clung to him a little hysterically, her tears spilling over on to her cheeks and dampening his spotless white shirt as she muttered incoherently and repeatedly, "You're alive! You're alive! Oh, thank God you're alive!"

"Take it easy, Anna." His hands were warm and firm against her shoulders as he held her away from him and stared down at her with a bewildered look in those usually perceptive eyes of his. "I'm alive, as you keep repeating, but I'd like to know why you imagined I wouldn't be."

"But . . . the plane . . . I spoke to the airport authorities not an hour ago, and – and they said –" She faltered to a confused stop, wondering vaguely why he was staring at her so strangely, but conscious only of the immense relief that he was safe. "Oh, Scott . . . if anything had happened to you, I –"

"Nothing has happened to me," he interrupted her with unnecessary harshness. "Now sit down a minute, and tell me what all this is about."

It was a command she could not ignore and, as he drew her down on to the sofa beside him, she began her halting explanation. "It was on the news – they lost radio contact with your plane. There was a storm and – it was reported missing."

"My God!" he exclaimed raspingly, his taut features strangely white. "Anna, I wasn't on that flight. I was held up unexpectedly in Durban, so I told Joshua and Bill to go on without me. They both know the business as well as I do, and there was no real urgency for me to be there as well."

"Oh, Scott," she sighed unsteadily, her hands gripping his tightly as she fought against the tears. "I've been nearly out of my mind at the thought –"

"We'll talk later," he said abruptly as he disengaged himself and got to his feet. "I have to telephone the airport authorities first."

Left alone in the living-room, Anna made an effort to pull herself together, but she found herself squirming inwardly at her complete lack of control when Scott appeared so unexpectedly before her. What he must have thought of her, she had no idea, and she felt the blood surge painfully into her pale cheeks when she realised how embarrassingly clear she had made her feelings when she had clung to him so desperately in her frenzied state of relief.

Shame brought her to her feet just as Scott replaced the receiver in the hall and, gathering the shattered remnants of her composure about her forcibly, she prepared herself to face him as he entered the living-room.

"Do they have any further news?" she asked in a voice that was not quite as controlled as she would have liked it to be.

"Nothing so far," he said, removing his jacket and tie, and undoing the top buttons of his shirt as he spoke. "They're still hoping that the pilot may have succeeded in landing the plane somewhere, but with the radio not functioning, and several telephone lines down in that area, it may take time for them to get a message through."

Her relief at finding Scott safe did not diminish her concern for the others in the missing aircraft. "You don't think that they may have had an – an accident?"

"The pilot is very experienced, and not the kind to take unnecessary chances. There's always the possibility that something unforeseen may have happened, but I'd rather not consider it until we've had more news," he said abruptly, not looking at her. "Where's Aunt Dorrie?"

"She's staying with the Fergusons at Port Shepstone for the weekend. That reminds me," she added quickly, "you'd better telephone and let her know you're safe.

The number is on the notepad beside the telephone, and you might give Morris and Sheila a ring as well. They were just as worried."

While Scott made the necessary calls, Anna stood about restlessly, and wondered just how this day would end. The dismal weather conditions seemed to continue as if in sympathy with her state of mind, and her hands shook when she smoothed down her skirt unnecessarily at the sound of Scott's footsteps approaching the living-room a few minutes later.

"Could I make you something to drink?" she asked nervously when he stood observing her with a disconcerting expression in his eyes. "Tea or coffee, perhaps?"

"Later," he gestured abruptly as he came towards her, and the room was suddenly not large enough to accommodate them both when he added: "While we're waiting for news we might as well spend the time getting a few things sorted out between ourselves, I think."

Anna felt herself go numb with cold, and a frightened little pulse quivered in her throat. Fear and anxiety had sapped her strength, and to hear him ask for his freedom would be more than she could bear at the moment, she thought as she shied away mentally from the subject.

"I don't think I want to discuss –"

"I love you, Anna."

There was a loud soaring in her ears while she stared at him speechlessly. A large part of her clamoured desperately to believe him, but she dared not – not yet, she thought as she swallowed nervously. "You're – you're just saying that because – because you feel obliged to after the way I – I –"

"You're wrong, my darling," he said quietly as she faltered helplessly. "It's something I should have told you right from the start, but I decided it could wait until you'd managed to rid yourself of the feelings you still had for Andrew Tait."

"But I don't love Andrew," she blurted out the truth. "The moment I saw him again I realised I didn't love him; that I never really loved him at all."

"Because you love me?" Scott suggested, his penetrating eyes probing hers relentlessly.

She turned away, unable to bear his intense scrutiny as she said flatly, "I think I've already made that perfectly obvious, haven't I?"

"Anna, Anna," he murmured her name in a voice that was vibrantly low as he drew her back against the hardness of his body. "The moment I heard of Joan's arrival in Amazibu Bay I realised I couldn't delay telling you how I felt about you. You had to know exactly where you stood in case her appearance caused you to have doubts, and I flew to Johannesburg with that purpose in mind."

Happiness began to flow through her veins like a heady wine as he turned her into his arms, and she buried her face against him as she confessed breathlessly, "I waited impatiently for you to come to Johannesburg after discovering that Andrew no longer meant anything to me. I knew then just how much I – I loved you, and I had to make you understand that somehow, but –"

"I saw you arriving back at the house with Andrew, and my flaming jealousy spoiled everything for both of us," Scott filled in for her as he held her closer, and raised her face to his, but when she avoided his lips, he asked: "What is it, my love?"

"If you love me as you say you do, then why did you humiliate me so much last night at the Ball?" she wanted to know, and the hours of pain and suffering were clearly visible in her eyes.

"I told you, Anna, it wasn't my intention to humiliate you," he said, his expression darkening as he released her and turned away, thrusting his hands into his pockets. "When Joan decided to latch on to me, my first reaction was to repulse her, but I happened to notice your expression, and I decided to pay you back in kind."

"You wanted to make me jealous?" she demanded incredulously.

"Yes." His glance was mocking when he turned to face her. "I succeeded, didn't I?"

Anna drew a shuddering breath, and clenched her hands convulsively. "I could have killed you, I was so furious!"

"My scheme backfired a little, I must admit," he smiled ruefully. "I couldn't get rid of Joan afterwards, and every time I wanted to dance with you, you happened to be dancing with someone else. I eventually couldn't take much more of Joan's behaviour, and she didn't care very much for the things I had to say to her."

"So that's why she went off in a huff," Anna murmured as understanding dawned.

"Anna . . ."

The appeal in his voice did not go unnoticed, but she was driven by an urgency now to clear the air completely. "You went to see Joan the other evening after she'd telephoned, didn't you?"

"Yes," he admitted, lighting a cigarette and drawing her down on to the sofa beside him, but Anna managed to keep some distance between them as he explained. "She wrote to me some weeks ago telling me her marriage was in trouble and asking for help, but I ignored her letter, and her repeated attempts to contact me since her arrival. When she telephoned the other evening, I knew I couldn't avoid her much longer, so I took that call, but she refused to explain anything and insisted that she had to see me and speak to me personally. I refused, at first, but I finally decided it would perhaps be the most logical thing to see her, and to find out exactly what the problem was. If she was really as unhappy as she wanted me to believe, then I would have considered helping her, but –"

"It wasn't a case of being unhappy, was it?" she suggested tentatively when he hesitated.

"No, it wasn't," he acknowledged, drawing hard on his cigarette. "Oh, she gave me some garbled account of how her husband had been unfaithful to her, that he refused to stay with her, and that she realised now what a mistake she'd made when she married him and not me, but I'm afraid I wasn't a very sympathetic listener and, after her veiled hints at a possible reunion, I made it quite clear that I had no further interest in her."

"Was her husband being unfaithful to her?"

"It was nothing like that at all," Scott said grimly. "I made a few enquiries and Dennis Mulder, God help him, still loves Joan and wants her back, but her irrational spending finally forced him to announce legally and publicly that he was no longer responsible for any debts incurred by his wife. There wasn't a place in Johannesburg who'd give her anything on credit after that, so she packed her bags and came here, hoping I would swallow her story."

"Poor Joan," Anna sighed, unable to prevent herself from feeling a twinge of pity for the woman who had been so instrumental in widening the gap between Scott and herself.

"Forget about her," Scott ordered, taking her hand and raising it to his lips. "Joan is most probably on her way back to her husband by now, and I'd much rather talk about us."

"After last night I was convinced you loved her," Anna commented, wincing as she recalled the pain and anguish of the hours she had spent tossing and turning on her bed.

"I never loved her, Anna. She chased me a little after Trudie died," he said bluntly, meeting her startled glance.

"You never loved her?"

"I was attracted to her before I met Trudie, and after Trudie died she was – available," he explained with a look of distaste on his face.

The telephone rang shrilly and Anna felt a chill of fear sweep through her as Scott went to answer it. 'Please, please, let the others be safe,' she prayed silently while she waited, and her anxious glance was raised to Scott's when he returned to her side.

"They were trapped by the storm and the mist after losing radio contact, and the pilot had to make a forced landing on a farm in the Ladysmith district," he explained, the grimness about his mouth diminishing. "The telephone lines were down, so they had to wait for a lift to Ladysmith before they could get a message through."

"They're all safe?"

"Yes, my love," he smiled with relief. "They're all safe."

"Thank God!" she sighed, going into his arms and burying her face against him. "How will they get back?"

"The radio has been repaired, and there's no damage to the aircraft, so as soon as the weather clears they'll refuel and go on to Lesotho as planned."

Her throat tightened as she thought of those terrifying moments when she had imagined Scott was in danger, and she snuggled closer to him, wrapping her arms about him tightly. "Darling, I died a thousand deaths thinking you might be injured, or –"

"Hush," he whispered urgently, sliding his hand round to the nape of her neck and pressing her head deeper into the comforting hollow of his shoulder. "Can you imagine now how I felt when I saw you being dragged out to sea?"

"I at least didn't half kill you when I found that you were safe," she laughed shakily, remembering the thorough shaking she had received once they had reached the safety of the beach.

"It was either that, or kiss you until you begged for mercy," he told her dryly, rubbing his cheek against her temple.

"I would have preferred the kiss, I think," she informed him in a muffled voice against his neck where she could feel the throbbing of his heart against her lips.

"Now she tells me!" he exclaimed mockingly.

"It's never too late to remedy the situation," she whispered, raising her lips to his.

He kissed her lingeringly with increasing passion, but as his arms tightened about her, her own words returned to haunt her. *It's never too late!* If Scott had been on that plane, and if something serious had happened to him, it *would* have been too late!

She shivered against him involuntarily and struggled against the warm pressure of his arms.

"What now, my love?" he demanded impatiently against her lips.

"I love you, and I shall always love you," she spoke with a note of urgency in her voice. "Don't let us ever part again, for any length of time, with a misunderstanding of any kind between us."

"Anna," he groaned her name, his lips seeking out the sensitive cord along her neck while he inhaled the subtle fragrance of her perfume.

"Do I have your word on that?" she demanded, her treacherous body responding to the sensations created by his exploring mouth.

"You have my word, my darling, my adorable wife," he murmured huskily, claiming her lips this time with an urgency that shook her to her very soul.

There was so much she still wanted to say, but for the moment it would have to wait, she decided as her lips moved beneath his with a matching hunger, and she surrendered herself to the emotions that swept through her like a hurricane wreaking havoc. Her desire mounted swiftly, and she drew away from him a little while she still had the strength to do so.

"Scott ..." she began breathlessly, avoiding his lips and holding him off with her hands against his broad chest where she could feel the quick, heavy beat of his heart. "Don't you want to know why I was with Andrew that evening when you arrived in Johannesburg?"

He frowned impatiently. "Does it matter now why you were with him?"

"If we're going to clear away all the misunderstandings, then we should do it properly," she insisted, disengaging herself from his arms and taking Andrew's letter from the pocket of her skirt. "Read this. It would, perhaps, explain it better than I could."

Scott unfolded the letter with a certain reluctance and read through it quickly, but he gave no indication of what he thought until he threw the letter aside and said: "So it was help and advice he'd wanted."

"Yes," she replied, avoiding the intensity of his searching glance as she recalled some of the other things Andrew had mentioned to her.

"Was it only help and advice that he wanted?" Scott demanded quietly, placing his hand beneath her chin and forcing her to meet his eyes, and it felt as though the heavy beat of her heart would choke her when she realised that the time had come to confess all.

Her eyes pleaded with him as she removed his hand from beneath her chin and placed her trembling lips against it briefly. "In Andrew's unhappy state of mind he imagined he'd made a mistake, and that he should have married me. He said he felt guilty, but he admitted, too, that he still loved Debbie, and when she later mentioned that same feeling of guilt to me, I realised I could help them after all by letting them know how much I cared for you. And ..." she swallowed nervously, "it worked!"

Scott's blue gaze probed hers relentlessly for interminable seconds, but she did not look away as she allowed him, for the first time, to see right into her heart.

"I'd like to believe what your eyes are telling me," he began eventually, "but are you sure your feelings for Andrew –"

"Don't!" she interrupted quickly, placing her fingers against his lips. "Don't torture yourself with unnecessary doubts. I was in love with an illusion, but this is reality – you and I."

"For always?"

"For always," she insisted fervently, throwing her arms about him and burying her face against his solid, dependable chest. "When you said 'Goodbye, Anna' in that peculiar way at Jan Smuts that day when I went to see you off, I imagined it was your way of making me understand that it was all over between us, and I just couldn't accept that. Not from you!"

His arms tightened about her and his kisses rained on her eyes, her cheeks and her quivering lips as he said: "My love, I was consumed with jealousy, and the fear of losing you. I was hardly aware of what I was saying at the time."

Anna drew his head down to hers and they exchanged a long and satisfying kiss that sent the blood pulsating madly through her veins.

"We've been such idiots, you and I," she whispered dreamily some time later.

"Such mad, crazy idiots," he admitted, his fingers unbuttoning her blouse while his lips explored the smoothness of her shoulder before purposely venturing lower to the swelling curve of her breast.

"I suppose we shall still have our arguments," she said unsteadily, her senses responding deliriously to his sensual caresses.

"Undoubtedly."

"But no more doubts, please?"

"No more doubts," Scott echoed, raising his head to look down at her with such a wealth of tenderness in his eyes that she felt weak with the intensity of her happiness. "I love you, Anna."

"And I love you," she whispered as his lips met hers, and despite the fact that it was raining outside, the sun was shining for her. The keeper of her heart had given her his heart in return.

Harlequin Salutes...

Essie Summers

with six of her best-selling
love stories.

- **Anna of Strathallan** (# 1917)
- **Not by Appointment** (# 2000)
- **Beyond the Foothills** (# 2021)
- **Goblin Hill** (# 2068)
- **Adair of Starlight Peaks** (# 2133)
- **Spring in September** (# 2148)

Each novel by this world-renowned
romance author is a captivating reading
experience. Each book, peopled
with warm and human characters, is
a romance that will reach out
and touch your heart.

You won't want to miss any
of these very special love stories.

Harlequin Salutes Essie Summers

COMPLETE AND MAIL THIS COUPON TODAY!

HARLEQUIN READER SERVICE

In U.S.A.
MPO Box 707
Niagara Falls, NY 14302

In Canada
Harlequin Reader Service
Stratford, Ontario N5A 6W2

Please send me the following editions of Harlequin Salutes ESSIE
SUMMERS. I am enclosing my check or money order for $1.25 for each
novel ordered, plus 59¢ to cover postage and handling.

☐ 1917 Anna of Strathallan   ☐ 2068 Goblin Hill
☐ 2000 Not by Appointment   ☐ 2133 Adair of Starlight Peaks
☐ 2021 Beyond the Foothills   ☐ 2148 Spring in September

Number of novels checked_____ $1.25 each = $_____

Postage and handling $_____ .59

New York State residents
please add appropriate sales tax $_____

                   TOTAL $_____

NAME_____
                 (Please Print)

ADDRESS_____

CITY_____

STATE/PROV._____

ZIP/POSTAL CODE_____

Offer expires March 31, 1981   R2358